PELICAN BOOKS

A941

# THE INNOVATORS

Michael Shanks was born in 1927 and educated at Blundells and Balliol College, Oxford, with a period of commissioned service in the Royal Artillery in between. After leaving Oxford he lectured in economics at a New England university (Williams College, Mass.), before becoming a journalist, first on the *Economist* and subsequently on the *Financial Times*, where he worked as industrial editor until 1964. During this time he published three books – *The Stagnant Society* (a Pelican book), *The Lessons of Public Enterprise*, and, with John Lambert, *Britain and the New Europe*, published in North America under the title *The Common Market Today – and Tomorrow*). His other publications include *How to Export* (Board of Trade), *ABC of Economics* (B.B.C. Publications), *The Future of the Sterling Area* (Fabian Society), *Incomes Policy and the Professional Employee* (National Union of Teachers), and *Poems* (Fantasy Press). He also contributed articles to a wide range of publications, and became well known as a TV and radio commentator and lecturer on current affairs. He travelled widely in Western and Eastern Europe, North America and Australasia. In July 1964 he joined the *Sunday Times* as economic correspondent and shortly afterwards was elected treasurer of the Fabian Society. At the beginning of 1965 he was seconded to the Department of Economic Affairs as Industrial Adviser to H.M. Government, and in May 1966 he became Co-ordinator of Industrial Policy. His secondment has recently expired. Michael Shanks is married and has four children.

MICHAEL SHANKS

---

# *The Innovators*

## THE ECONOMICS
## OF
## TECHNOLOGY

PENGUIN BOOKS

Penguin Books Ltd, Harmondsworth, Middlesex, England
Penguin Books Inc., 3300 Clipper Mill Road, Baltimore, Md 21211, U.S.A.
Penguin Books Australia Ltd, Ringwood, Victoria, Australia

—

First published 1967
Copyright © Michael Shanks, 1967

—

Made and printed in Great Britain by
Cox & Wyman Ltd, London, Reading and Fakenham
Set in Monotype Imprint

FOR MY CHILDREN
To redeem a rash pledge

# CONTENTS

PREFACE                                                9

1. *After the Age of Miracles*                        15
2. *The United States – Challenge and Response*       43
3. *The United States – A Problem of Balance*         73
4. *The United States – Lessons for Europe*           90
5. *Government as Innovator*                          102
6. *The Management of Innovation*                     191
7. *The Organization of Change*                       239

POSTSCRIPT                                            273
APPENDIX                                              277
INDEX                                                 283

Nor is it shameful to aver
A vague desire to be about
Where the important things occur. . . .

William Empson, *Autumn on Nan-Yueh*

# PREFACE

THIS book has had a long and tortuous birth. It began when I visited the United States, at the end of 1963, as the guest of Arthur D. Little Inc., the contract research firm. At that time I was interested in writing a short book about the contract research industry in the United States, and its possible relevance to Britain. However, as I started to write the book in 1964 it became clear to me that the theme I really wanted to explore was Innovation – what factors in the organization and motivation of the individual company and of society at large either encourage or retard it. This, essentially, is what this book is about.

My basic message can be summed up in a few sentences. There is a wide gap in every country between the knowledge of new products, processes and techniques and the successful application of that knowledge in industry. To paraphrase Rousseau: 'Man has mastered the secrets of scientific production. Yet almost everywhere he fails to exploit them adequately.' It is the job of technology to bridge that gap. The gap is not just a matter of ignorance, however. It is also made up (to switch the metaphor) of a whole series of barriers: barriers of company and social structure, of educational traditions and methods, of human and industrial relations, of social and cultural values, and so on and so on. The company, and the country, that can best overcome these barriers and bridge the gap between knowledge and application will succeed in the economic struggle; those that fail will go under. The issue is crucial for our national survival. But neither at company nor at national level can the opportunities presented by modern technology be grasped without a clear and conscious strategy, and without accepting all the implications of change.

This book, then, is about the strategy and tactics of innovation, at company and national level. It is about automation, about management, about research and development, the role

9

of the scientist in industry and society, about planning for growth, about the relations between government and industry; it is about all these things, and more, for all are relevant to the theme of innovation and change. Some many-faceted subjects, such as regional planning, for example, are looked at in this book through specifically technological 'spectacles'. Others, despite their relevance to the theme, have had to be ignored through lack of either space or knowledge. For example, I am conscious of the omission of any discussion of the impact of taxation on company structure, and therefore on the possible pace of innovation. This exclusion is deliberate, for I feel that it is still too early to assess the long-term impact of the revolutionary tax changes of 1965 and 1966. But there are no doubt other vital omissions and errors which are the product of inadvertence, and which readers and reviewers will bring to my notice.

The book was roughly half-finished when the general election of October 1964 took place, and I was invited to join the newly formed Department of Economic Affairs as an industrial adviser on secondment from my employers, the *Sunday Times*. It had to be set aside until the early months of 1966, when it was hastily completed in preparation for the ending of my secondment in July 1966. However, in May 1966 the then Chief Industrial Adviser at the D.E.A., Mr Fred Catherwood, was appointed Director-General of the National Economic Development Office and I was invited to succeed him at the D.E.A., my secondment being extended for a further twelve months in consequence. The book therefore had to be put aside a second time, to be finally completed and revised earlier this year.

This is not an ideal method for writing a book which is intended to be topical. It has been a product of work at weekends and in the evenings after a long day's work, and only the forbearance and tolerance of my wife and children has made this unsatisfactory procedure possible. On the other hand the book may have gained something from the delays to which it has been subjected, for my work in the Government these past two and a half years has given me many insights into this most complex of problems which I could hardly have obtained elsewhere; and I will be eternally grateful to my colleagues in the D.E.A., and particularly to my former chief Fred Catherwood, for having afforded me this unique and stimulating opportunity.

The reticence proper to a civil servant has, I hasten to say, guided me in my writing on those matters falling within the period of my sojourn in Whitehall. I have taken care in this book not to quote from or refer to any unpublished documents, nor to reveal any state secrets or the contents of privileged meetings or conversations. The conclusions can in no way be taken to reflect the views of any person or organization other than myself.

Because of the protean nature of the subject, and the convolutions through which the book has gone in the course of its writing, I have not found it easy in the time at my disposal to fasten it into a logically watertight structure. Inevitably, too, it is impressionistic rather than encyclopedic, in places no doubt superficial. For these defects of which I am conscious – and for others, no doubt, of which I am not – I apologize in advance, with a few words of preliminary self-defence. First, I am not by training a scientist or an engineer; therefore, as the sub-title indicates, this book is not about technology as such but about 'The *Economics* of Technology'. Second, although in the course of the book I mention various companies, organizations and techniques by name, I do so merely to illustrate points in the text. I am not seeking, as I indicated above, to provide a comprehensive guide to business techniques, to consultants, or indeed to anything else. I am conscious that some organizations and some people for whom I have a warm regard and admiration may feel that they have been slighted by not receiving a mention when others, no more worthy, do receive one. Again, let me apologize in advance and make clear that mention in these pages is not meant to confer an accolade, nor omission the opposite.

The organization of the book is, I think, relatively straight-forward. Chapter 1 discusses the relevance of technology to

Britain's economic performance in the period up to October 1964. Chapters 2 and 3 discuss recent U.S. experience – Chapter 2 at the company level, Chapter 3 at the level of national policy. Chapter 4 briefly draws the threads of the two preceding chapters together, and considers the lessons for Britain. In the last – and longest – three chapters we return to the United Kingdom. Chapter 5 picks up the economic story from the October 1964 election, and discusses the role of government – in the light of our experience since then – in promoting innovation; necessarily, it concentrates on the work of the D.E.A. and the Ministry of Technology. Chapter 6 deals with developments in, and problems of, management; Chapter 7 with the implications of technological advance for the labour force (which includes all of us) and the attendant problems. Within this general framework the assignment of particular subjects to particular chapters may seem a trifle arbitrary – and I would be the last to claim that the arrangement of subject-matter could not be improved. But a certain amount of overlap is, I believe, inherent in the nature of the subject, because of the way in which things interconnect with each other in this field.

Rather to my surprise, I find on re-reading the text that the general mood of the book, so far as the United Kingdom is concerned, is one of modest optimism. We have taken so many batterings to our national self-esteem in recent years – some self-inflicted – that it is pleasant to be able to record one's conviction that we do seem, in this vital area at any rate, to be moving in the right direction. We have, of course, a very long way to go; we cannot afford to dawdle. But we have made a start.

My obligations and debts to others in the preparation of this book are manifold, and I despair of recording them all here. My wife has been consistently understanding and encouraging. Ann Scott has undertaken the typing with speed and efficiency. I am deeply grateful to Arthur D. Little Inc. for inspiration and assistance, and particularly to Michael Michaelis for guiding me through the mazes of Washington D.C. Much of the material in the book draws heavily on articles originally prepared in other contexts for the *Financial Times* (where the chart on page 58 originally appeared) and the *Director*, and I am grateful to both journals for allowing me to make fresh use of this material. The appendix on the London School of Business Studies syllabus appears by kind permission of the director, Dr A. F. Earle. I have benefited greatly from reading Geoffrey Owen's excellent Penguin, *Industry in the U.S.A.* (1966), and have drawn liberally on it for information and guidance. Among other recent books which have influenced me I should perhaps make special mention of Andrew Shonfield's path-breaking *Modern Capitalism* (R.I.I.A./Oxford, 1965).

I have pillaged widely and shamelessly from journalistic sources, in particular from the admirable *Journal of Scientific Management* and *Management Today*, and from the excellent articles by Patrick Coldstream and Geoffrey Owen in the 'World of Management' series in the *Financial Times*. I have tried to acknowledge these plunders seriatim, but may not have succeeded in all cases. I would like therefore to take this opportunity of expressing to these authorities the sense of gratitude which must be shared by all serious students of this subject.

But above all I wish to express my thanks to Alcon Copisarow, to S. C. Leslie, and to certain colleagues in government who must remain anonymous, for invaluable assistance in criticizing and improving my text and for innumerable insights into this complex and baffling subject. Neither they, nor any others mentioned in this preface, are in any way responsible for the opinions and conclusions in this book, still less for the errors which no doubt remain. But I can assure my readers that without their guidance and intervention it would have been a good deal worse!

*Little Kingshill, June 1967*                                    M.J.S.

# CHAPTER ONE

# AFTER THE AGE OF MIRACLES

EVERY story has to begin somewhere. I propose to begin this one, for no pressing logical reason beyond convenience, at one of the lesser climacterics of recent prehistory, the seventeenth regular meeting of the National Economic Development Council (hereafter referred to as 'Neddy'). This meeting, held on 4 December 1963, on the fifteenth floor of the Vickers building on Millbank overlooking the Thames, witnessed the first (and unsuccessful) attempt in recent years to secure an agreed incomes policy. Much water has flowed under many bridges since that far-off day – though how far we have advanced towards a real solution of our problems in the process remains inevitably a matter for debate. But my reason for concentrating attention on this particular meeting is that it represented a moment of truth in the examination of the forces playing upon the modern British economy – or indeed any modern economy. It represented the, somewhat belated, recognition that the Age of Miracles was over.

## The 'Wirtschaftswunder' Era

The 1950s saw the biggest economic transformation of any decade which the world has yet known. The trail-blazer, West Germany, moved rapidly from the war-torn shambles of the ruined Third Reich into a sleek, efficient, affluent society with a higher living standard than Britain's. Germany's achievement was paralleled and in some cases surpassed by other non-Communist nations – by Japan, Italy and France among the larger powers, as well as by some smaller countries like Switzerland, the Netherlands and Austria. ('Ours', say the Austrians proudly, 'was the only *real* economic miracle; we don't even work!') In each case these countries achieved regular increases in national income of $4\frac{1}{2}$ per cent or more per annum. Germany's average annual increase was in fact around $7\frac{1}{2}$ per cent, Japan's higher. The result was an explosion of economic growth throughout most of the western European continent, and in some places elsewhere, which transformed the whole social structure of the region and also helped to pull the rest of the world's economy up with it.

The rate of economic growth varied from country to country, and some of the advanced industrial nations failed markedly to share in the general advance. Prominent among these laggards were the great Anglo-Saxon powers, Britain and America. But the reasons in each case were different. The United States started off with a very much higher standard of living than Europe, and her main problem was to create a high enough level of consumer demand to keep her industries fully occupied. There were other factors involved too. The high cost of American labour made it hard for U.S. firms to compete effectively in export markets with the lower-cost industries of Europe and Japan. Also, there were and are substantial pockets of poverty in the United States – in the Appalachian region, among the Negro minority and in parts of the farming community in particular – the existence of which depresses the total level of consumer spending. The importance of these factors will be discussed at greater length later in this book. But the great bogey confronting the U.S. economy in the fifties was the bogey of consumer saturation due to affluence – the fact that industry could produce the goods quicker than the salesman could persuade the customer to buy them. America had a chequered rate of growth in the fifties; the brakes to expansion, when they came, came primarily as a result of consumer indigestion and repletion.

Britain's case was different. The British standard of living at the beginning of the fifties was fairly high, but it was far from being the highest in Europe. It was exceeded by at least three countries – Sweden, Switzerland and Luxembourg – and roughly equalled by three others – Belgium, Denmark and Norway; almost all these countries have subsequently grown appreciably faster than Britain.

It is notoriously difficult to compare living standards in different countries accurately; not only do relative prices, tax rates and so on vary, but so do consumer preferences and the way in which people spend what money they have. Nevertheless, at the time of the Neddy meeting it seems clear that Britain was running in about thirteenth place in the world stakes of gross national product per head of population – behind the United States, Canada, New Zealand, Australia, Kuwait, Qatar, Sweden, Switzerland, Luxembourg, Denmark, West Germany and France (not necessarily in that order). This represented a drop of three places since 1953. What was more disturbing was the fact that if existing productivity trends in the various countries were to continue, by the early 1970s the average Briton would find himself worse off than almost all his Continental cousins, and on a roughly comparable level with the average Russian, Venezuelan or Israeli. The implications do not need spelling out.

(In an article in *Lloyds Bank Review* in January 1966 the economist Angus Maddison argued: ·

It seems likely that British industrial productivity is now below that of all West European countries north of the Alps, and probably not very much different from the levels in the U.S.S.R., Italy and Japan. Just as the other countries have exploited and, to some extent, can still exploit backward agriculture as a source of growth, so the United Kingdom has a good deal of backwardness to remove in industry.

Maddison's article goes on to recognize explicitly the special constraints under which the British economy has laboured since the war: notably the high defence spending and the problems associated with running sterling as an international reserve currency – problems which fall outside the scope of this book. But he concludes, surely correctly, that to counteract these constraints – since they were, at least in the short term, unavoidable – a 'bigger policy effort than in other countries' was required. Easy to say: but, as we shall see, less easy to achieve.

At all events, nobody who lived in Britain through the fifties would conclude that there was any obvious lack of consumer demand. By and large, the British consumer was prepared to buy as much as industry could provide. The problem was too much demand for goods rather than too little. Why then did Britain's growth rate falter and flag? In the event the progress of the British economy was as jerky as America's, but the reasons were diametrically different. British booms did not die, as American ones did, of their own accord; they were killed off deliberately by government action. In 1952, 1955, 1957 and again in 1960 British Chancellors of the Exchequer deliberately engineered recessions or periods of stagnation by applying curbs to capital investment and/or consumer spending. (The process was to be repeated by a reluctant Labour government in 1965, and again more savagely in 1966.) They did this because they felt, rightly or wrongly, that the boom in the domestic economy was getting out of hand, that our costs were rising faster than our output, that our prices were rising faster than our competitors', that the demands of the home market were sucking in more imports than we could afford and drawing away the extra exports needed to pay for them. In other words, the paramount problem of the British economy – so it was felt in the fifties – was inflation. Hence the subsequently much-criticized alternation of 'stop—go' in British economic policy during this decade.

It is not hard to criticize this policy. In fact, it is clear in retrospect that government intervention in the 1950s was not on the whole well-timed or well-planned. So, far from acting as a Keynesian stabilizer, government – largely through errors of timing – was probably on balance a de-stabilizing element in the economy in the fifties.[1] Moreover, damping down the home market did not on the whole succeed in reducing costs or boosting exports. When the government increased taxes in the hope of cutting down home consumption, it merely stimulated the trade unions to claim higher wages to offset the increased cost of living. Employers, aware that government policy was liable to change again fairly rapidly – that every 'stop' would be followed by a 'go' as soon as it seemed safe to do so – preferred to hang on to their workers during the bad periods rather than run the risk of being short-staffed when demand picked up. Consequently the unions' bargaining power remained strong even in the recessions, and their demands for wage increases were usually reasonably successful. But the government's policy prevented home demand from expanding, and since employment did not drop with production the level of productivity actually declined. This meant that in order to pay increased wages in return for static or declining sales, employers either had to eat into profits or raise prices. To some extent at least they preferred to do the latter. Thus demand inflation was replaced by cost inflation. Britain's prices did not become more competitive, nor did exports receive their expected boost.

Another factor tending in the same direction was the growing importance in the economy of highly capitalized industries like steel, chemicals and motor cars, where the bulk of costs comes from fixed overheads, while those costs which vary with the level of production – e.g. labour and materials – form a fairly small proportion of the total. In these industries the higher the rate of capacity utilization the greater the profit – or, to put it another way, the lower the unit cost. Consequently, in boom periods these industries can afford to lower their prices, while if demand falls off so that their capacity utilization drops below break-even point they may have to put prices up. These industries therefore suffer particularly badly from 'stop–go', and it was unfortunate from the point of view of Britain's economic growth in the fifties that it was precisely these expanding industries which bore the main impact of the government's restrictive policies.[2]

Finally, there is no doubt at all that the choppings and changes of government policy dictated by short-term crises slowed down the rate of capital investment in British industry, and therefore adversely affected long-term growth and competitiveness. Not only did the restrictions in some cases directly impede investment; even where they were directed towards consumer spending they prevented firms from earning their projected return on the investments they had already undertaken and so diminished their ability or willingness to expand further. In 1955 and again in 1960 a capital investment boom was superimposed on a consumer spending boom. In each case the boom was followed by a three-year period of stagnation initiated or intensified by government action. This meant that the new capital equipment installed took far longer to pay off than anticipated, and during these periods of stagnation, when there were in fact labour and material resources available, industry was for the most part reluctant to employ them to undertake further investment on any big scale. (The same sad process was to recur five years later under a Labour government which had come to power pledged to abolish 'stop–go'.)

This had two consequences. First, the capital investment cycle, instead of complementing or offsetting the consumer spending cycle, was superimposed on it. Investment demand occurred at precisely the times when the economy could least easily absorb the extra strain on resources. Second, industry was made more cautious about incurring capital expenditure by its lack of confidence in the stability of government economic policy. Obsessed – understandably – by short-term problems, and insufficiently aware of the climate of modern business management, government officials failed to realize that a major capital investment project can only pay for itself over a number of years, and that if industry fears that its calculations of future demand are liable to be overthrown by some totally unforeseen

and unforeseeable switch in government policy, it will tend
always to play for safety and try to avoid the risks involved in
expansion.

Investment, in short, has a dual aspect. In the short term it
imposes strains on manpower resources and on the capital goods
industries, adding to the pressure of demand, diverting resources
from exports and adding to imports. In the long term it is the
one means by which the economy can be so strengthened that it
is able to avoid these problems in its efforts to grow. Britain in
the fifties and, so far, in the sixties has tended to get the worst
of both worlds. We have invested too little; yet our efforts to
correct this have periodically imposed strains on the economy
which have proved insupportable.

The arguments against the kind of 'stop-go' economic policies commonly practised in the fifties are, therefore, formidable.
But it has proved easier to point out the deficiencies than to
evolve a workable alternative. One powerful school of thought,
associated particularly with the name of Professor Frank Paish,
argues that what is required is a permanent unused reserve of
labour and capital in order to keep down the pressure of demand
on resources, and thereby costs. In fact this policy, largely
because of its electoral implications, has been applied only inter-
mittently in post-war Britain, despite its influence with the
Treasury. Its appeal to politicians has tended to weaken as the
time for general elections draws near. It is arguable that some of
the drawbacks of 'stop-go' could have been avoided had it been
maintained more persistently. But it seems unlikely. The most
obvious consequence of running the economy below capacity
for a prolonged period would be to raise unit costs in capital-
intensive industries, to reduce the demand for capital investment
and to hold back the growth of those industries on which the
future progress of an economy like Britain's must increasingly
depend.[2] These major defects must be set against the probable
benefit of some diversion of goods from the home market to
exports and a reduction in demand for imports – and a possible,

but on the record so far unproven, curb on the demands of the unions for wage increases. (In fact, as we shall see, it would be likely to diminish wage drift rather than the pressure for basic wage rises.)

It does not, unfortunately, follow from all this that a policy of straightforward economic expansion – 'go' without 'stop', or the antithesis of the Paish approach – would have seen Britain out of her troubles in the fifties. (It demonstrably failed to do so in the 1963–5 period.) In those periods when industry's expansionist tendencies were given full rein, imports invariably rose faster than exports, and prices faster than production. The expansionist argument is that if governments had not in each case lost their nerve all would have been well. In due course the injection of new capital into industry would have produced its reward in the form of a flood of new, cheaper products which would displace imports and win new export business.

On this too, one can only say that the argument is at best un-proven – and the risks of experimentation are obviously far greater in the 'dash for growth' policy than in its antithesis. The sterling crises which have dogged Britain ever since the war, and which were to reach a new climax after the Labour govern-ment took over in late 1964, are a permanent reminder of Britain's vulnerability. Few of our leading creditors are believers in the 'dash for growth' theory. Second, investment in new plant and machinery, though a necessary condition of greater eco-nomic efficiency, is hardly a sufficient one. It is not enough to invest; one must invest in the right things, at the right time, and in the right way. Britain in the fifties and early sixties, both in the public and the private sector, provides too many examples of capital investment wasted by inadequate management, inade-quate market research, inadequate labour relations – not to mention the additional problems caused by the vagaries of government policy – to enable one to feel that more invest-ment at this time, *per se*, would have solved our payments problems.[3]

What emerges from this brief and inevitably over-simplified run-down of Britain's economic failures of the fifties and early sixties? First, that the main obstacle to a faster rate of economic growth was not any lack of demand but a permanently weak balance-of-payments position which compelled the government periodically to cut back domestic expansion. Second, that neither the policies of the brake nor the policies of the accelerator, nor alternation between the two, appeared able to solve this basic problem. Third, the answer must therefore lie (assuming there *was* an answer!) in improving the basic efficiency and competitiveness of British industry – in looking, to pursue the motoring metaphor, not at the brake or accelerator but at the state of the engine. Fourth, that there must be a closer coordination between government and industry, and that in particular government must seek to provide more *continuity* of economic policy – to create a climate in which industry would be able to plan ahead with a degree of confidence, would be willing to expand and install new capital equipment, but where there would be enough competition to ensure that business remained dynamic and efficient.

## Neddy's Birth and Aspirations

In the early sixties some sort of consensus of opinion to this effect emerged – to some extent consciously, to some extent subconsciously – in Britain; and out of this consensus Neddy was born.

Neddy represented an exercise in voluntary cooperative national economic planning. It had four main roles. First, by building a model of the national implications of a particular growth target – the target actually chosen by Neddy was an expansion of 4 per cent per annum – it sought to help to reduce the area of uncertainty facing individual firms, and enable them to plan ahead with a greater knowledge of what their suppliers, their competitors and their customers would be doing and requiring. In this respect the work of an organization like Neddy represents an extension of the market research function which most firms now recognize as essential in forward planning. Accurate market research becomes more important, and more difficult, in proportion to the rate of change in the economy. This is a point to which we shall return more than once in this book. At the start of the sixties three things were happening in British industry: competition was becoming more acute (partly because of over-investment at the peak of the 1955 and 1959 booms), profit margins were coming under growing pressure, and the pace of technological innovation was accelerating. All these factors made it at once more urgent and more difficult to foresee the future with greater clarity. This was one major reason why British industrialists as a whole, despite their traditional inhibitions about government intrusion, not only welcomed Neddy but were among the first sections of the community to press for its establishment.

Neddy's second major role was to act as a permanent pressure group or lobby for economic growth – partly in industry, but more important within the government machine. It seems likely that Neddy played some part in persuading business executives to shed their inhibitions about growth and to plan for a faster rate of expansion in their individual enterprises than they would otherwise have done. But the extent to which this happened is far from clear. Certainly it was a less important factor than in France in the early post-war years, when the French *Commissariat Général du Plan* – Neddy's inspiration and exemplar – succeeded in converting the most cautious and stagnant industrial Establishment in Europe to a policy of dynamic expansion. In Britain, ten years later, there was neither the same need nor the same opportunity. The gospel which needed to be preached to British industry – and which still needs to be preached – was not the simple one: 'Expand!', which the French planners preached to their entrepreneurs in the Monnet era. It was, and is, rather: 'Modernize!' – a more complex commandment and one which this book seeks, in part at least, to elucidate. It is a gospel which Neddy in its first phase did disappointingly little to propagate.

Where, however, Neddy's persuasive or lobbying function *was* important was in Whitehall. Until Neddy's inception there was no body or organization in government with a specific responsibility for, or interest in, seeing that the economy was expanding. The senior economic department was the Treasury, whose prime function was to look after the balance of payments and the regulation of the national accounts. The objectives of economic policy in the fifties were, in this order, a strong pound, stable prices, and full employment. Neddy added a new responsibility and a new objective, and in this way provided a new dimension for government economic policy. (A significant internal reorganization of the Treasury machine in late 1962 helped to ensure a higher priority for the consideration of economic growth.) The speed with which this was accepted tended to disguise its revolutionary nature and its far-reaching implications for government. (We shall have more to say about this later on.)

Neddy's third function, and in some ways the most complex and important, was to set out the conditions which would be required to enable the economy to grow faster. This it did first in the so-called 'Orange Book' – *Conditions Favourable to Faster Growth* – the companion-piece to its so-called 'Green Book' – *Growth of the United Kingdom Economy to 1966* – which contained the model-building exercise.[4] It is clear that if a fully employed economy is to step up its rate of growth without inflation, it must become more efficient. Neddy's Orange Book contained a large number of recommendations, in the field of training, mobility, use of labour, development area policy, tax policy, and so on, to make the British economy more efficient, and therefore more readily able to expand without running into inflationary pressures or labour shortages. Unfortunately, as we shall see, Neddy's organization did not provide it with the means to see that its excellent prescripts were translated into action. In default of any effective follow-up system, it appeared only too often to be preaching to the wind.

This brings us to Neddy's fourth function, which follows logically from the first three. By its nature Neddy represented a partnership between government, industry and trade unions – a means by which these different sections of the body politic could be brought together, mutually educated as to the consequences of their actions and as to the ways in which they could cooperate to achieve the mutually-agreed growth target, and by which they could be made to recognize the implications of their own commitment to the plan. This mutually educative role was, and is, of overriding importance. We have seen how, during the fifties, partly through ignorance and partly through wrong-thinking, government economic policy tended to frustrate industry's plans instead of furthering them. With the establish-ment of Neddy a significant change occurred. Government policies began to reflect a greater awareness of industry's needs, particularly the need for continuity. This process of mutual education and communication is of crucial importance in the running of a modern economy, and it needs to be carried much further in the years ahead. This is a theme which will keep recurring in later chapters. The Neddy exercise, if it did nothing else (and it *did* do much else), would have justified itself by its achievement in setting this very necessary process in motion. (I do not want to go too deeply here into '*post hoc ergo propter hoc*' arguments. How much of the new thinking stemmed from Neddy, how much was generated elsewhere, are matters beyond the scope of this book.)

However, as the Chancellor of the Exchequer, Mr Reginald Maudling, soon began to complain, it was no good for the govern-ment to accept Neddy's medicine if the other partners did not do likewise. In fact the government's acceptance of the Orange Book was less complete than Mr Maudling liked to claim; nevertheless he had a point. It was one thing for the leaders of industry and the T.U.C. on the Neddy Council to approve the plans for growth and the measures which would be needed to realize them. It was another thing to accept the consequences of this approval for their own organizations and to act accordingly. During 1963 the government came increasingly to feel that its industrial partners were not playing their part. And towards the end of the year the Chancellor decided that the time had come to start applying the pressure.

The point at which pressure was to be applied was incomes policy – by which is meant an agreed formula for relating the overall growth of incomes (particularly wages) in the community to the growth of production. The importance of this hardly needs stressing. If wages and other incomes rise faster than output in any society, there must sooner or later be a rise in prices – and, if a country's price level rises faster than its competitors', sooner or later it will face balance-of-payments difficulties. This was a lesson which needed no stressing in the Britain of the late fifties and sixties. Clearly, therefore, if the growth of the country's production was to be planned, there was a cast-iron logical case for planning the growth of incomes too. For one thing, the rate of increase of incomes must play a big part (to put it no higher) in determining the rate of growth of consumer spending, which is the biggest single outlet for national production. Even more important, the rate of growth of incomes in a very real sense determines the rate of growth of production that can be afforded – and vice versa. Income planning and investment or production planning are the two sides of the one coin.

But, because of the legacy of mistrust between the unions and government arising out of the government's attempts to restrain wage increases unilaterally during the fifties, the T.U.C. at first refused to sanction the discussion of incomes policy in Neddy. It was always clear, to all parties, that sooner or later this taboo would have to be breached. All parties accepted the need for some form of incomes policy; and, if there were to be such a policy, the ideal forum for its negotiation would be the Neddy Council, where all the relevant interests were represented and where the negotiation of an incomes policy could be carried out in conjunction with all the other aspects of national planning. The only question was whether the complexities of the issue, and the deep smouldering resentments between unions and government which it would be bound to re-kindle, would be-tween them not only make agreement impossible at this stage but would also – by advertising its ultimate impotence – destroy the mystique, and damage the effectiveness, of Neddy as such.

The question was one of political judgement. On the one hand were those who urged that the nettle was still too hot to grasp, that Neddy should prove itself on other issues first and slowly build up the climate of cooperation and success which would eventually enable this last hurdle to be surmounted. On the other hand was the voice of the government urging per-sistently that without an agreed incomes policy the Neddy target could not be achieved without severe inflation – and under-estimating the obstacles in the way. Mr Maudling decided to take the bull by the horns. Neddy was dragged willy-nilly to Becher's Brook.

We have now arrived back, in our narrative, at the point at which we started – the meeting of 4 December 1963. In the round trip we have ignored many points of interest and rele-vance along the way – for example, the extent to which the approaching general election complicated the incomes policy issue, making the government more eager for a deal with the unions, and the T.U.C. more wary about committing itself to an agreement with the Conservative enemy which might em-barrass its political allies in the Labour Party. I am not setting out here to tell the whole story, either of Britain's economic failures in the fifties, or of the Neddy experiment, or of the debate on incomes policy. I mention them here only in so far as they are relevant to the main theme of this book, which is the economic and social background to innovation.

## Cold Facts on Overheating

The Neddy meeting on incomes policy produced two main reactions. First, the union leaders pointed out that they could only agree to a voluntary limitation on wages on two conditions: they must be assured that other sections of the community would not benefit from their restraint – in other words that there would be no net redistribution of the national income away from wages. This required some control or voluntary limitation on dividends – since a limitation on industry's wages bill would, *ceteris paribus*, tend to boost profits. They must also be assured that the real value of wages would not fall. This required some control or voluntary limitation on price increases. (In fact, though this was not brought out, the second requirement virtually comprehended the first; if prices were held down, there would presumably be no net increase in profits other than through increasing productivity – in which case wages too would rise.)[5] The employers' representatives undertook to see if a scheme could be worked out to regulate prices and profits. Three months later they were to report back that no scheme acceptable to industry had presented itself; the union leaders thereupon declared themselves absolved from any obligation to press forward with any scheme for regulating wages, and the whole discussion lapsed – until in the crisis months after October 1964, Prince Charming arrived to awaken the Sleeping Beauty in the virile guise of Mr George Brown.

The second major reaction at the December meeting came from the employers. The meeting was treated to a succession of managerial *cris de cœurs* almost embarrassing, according to observers, in their fervour and poignancy. 'How can we in our firms', went the refrain, 'refuse to pay the market rate for our workers, when we know damned well that if we don't they'll simply move up the road to other firms who will?'

The employers were, of course, right. The government's view, that wages could be kept down by simple agreement between employers and unions irrespective of the demand and supply position for manpower, was too *simpliste*. In fact wage levels, in any society, are determined by two forces. First, there is the cost-push pressure from organized labour, which normally operates through raising the basic wage – pushing the whole structure up from the bottom, as it were. This pressure can of course be neutralized by an effective national incomes policy.

The other force determining wage levels is the demand-pull of the market – the phenomenon known as 'wage-drift', whereby employers, in conditions of labour shortage, pay what they must to keep or attract the workers they need irrespective of trade union agreements or national wage rates. In this respect the price of labour, like that of any other commodity, is determined by supply and demand. This force tends to pull the wage structure up from the top, as it were, the typical beneficiaries being those workers who are in a locality or a profession where their gifts are particularly in demand; skilled men and women normally benefit from wage-drift much more than unskilled.

Of course these two aspects of the wage problem interact on one another. Naturally trade union bargaining strength is greater if labour is scarce than if it is abundant (though a strong trade union can often bargain successfully even in a buyer's market for labour). Moreover, a general wage increase, by generating new purchasing power and so increasing demand for goods, may itself lead to labour shortages which promote wage-drift. In recent years in Britain wage inflation has in fact proceeded by a sort of ratchet process; specific wage increases given by employers to specific groups of workers in specific places to meet specific shortages are then translated, by union pressure, into nation-wide increases; when that has been done the differential has to be restored in the initial problem areas for the same reason that it was originally given. This vicious spiral, with its origins in the boom areas of London and the Midlands, has been a feature of recent British society. It follows that if we are to get economic growth without inflation we must ensure a more even spread of work and prosperity throughout the country, and avoid the regional disparities which have characterized not only the British but most industrial economies in the last decade. (Hence the Labour government's proposal in April 1967 for a Regional Employment Premium to subsidize manufacturing employment in the development areas).

There are those who say that demand and supply are the only factors affecting the price of labour – that if the demand and supply of labour are not in balance an incomes policy is unworkable (because of wage-drift), and if they are in balance it is unnecessary. I reject this argument, for the reasons given above. Trade union wage pressure is itself one of the factors determining the overall demand for labour. Moreover, a certain amount of wage-drift is not only unavoidable but healthy, since it is only by offering higher rates that labour can be induced to move to those jobs and areas where it is needed, and where its productivity will be highest. A real wage freeze for more than short periods is not only unworkable in a free labour market (as the Dutch, and indeed the Communist countries, have found); it is also undesirable, since it would imply a brake on new enterprise. But basic wage increases negotiated by trade unions over a broad industrial field, largely independently of market forces, do not have this beneficial regulatory effect. There is therefore a strong case for trying to negotiate an overall incomes policy despite the inevitability of some wage-drift.

The operative word here, however, is 'some'. If the supply of labour is less than the demand over the economy as a whole, there will be wage inflation irrespective of the policy of the unions towards basic wages. Indeed, in these conditions the pressures on the union leaders to demand more wages could well prove irresistible, and the incomes policy itself therefore unworkable. Both, therefore, are desirable – an incomes policy to restrain the cost-push pressures on wages, an overall balance between demand and supply of labour to keep the demand-pull pressures down to reasonable dimensions.

The problem is, of course, to keep the demand for labour down to the level of supply when one is seeking to expand production from an initial situation of full employment. The Paishian approach, discussed above, is to keep the demand for labour a little *below* the available supply by restricting demand for goods. (This policy was to become the orthodoxy of the Labour government in the crisis of July 1966.) We have seen the limitations of this approach as applied in post-war Britain. But the argument against it goes deeper than this. Economic growth is, one cannot stress too much, a good thing in itself; it is what economics is all about. It is not an expendable luxury, to be set aside as and when it conflicts with other desiderata. (Neither of course can it be regarded as the *only* objective, to which all others must be subordinated.) There can always be room for argument about desirable *rates* of growth, and about the reconciliation of growth with other objectives. But we have to face the fact that no regime which does not succeed in enriching its people over the years will survive in the modern world except by virtue of bayonets or repression, nor will it deserve to survive. In all countries and continents of the world men have seen visions of a better and richer life, and they will not rest until they see these visions realized. We call this 'the revolution of rising expectations'. This phrase is usually applied to the underdeveloped and developing nations of Afro–Asia and Latin America, the under-privileged two thirds of mankind. But it applies, to my mind, equally in all countries. We need a faster rate of economic growth for at least four reasons. We need it, first, to meet our own in-dividual – possibly selfish – needs for better material conditions: needs constantly stimulated by an increasingly sophisticated and persuasive advertising industry. We need it, also, to meet the growing social needs of modern society – the needs of our old, our sick, our children; the need to improve and rebuild the basic infra-structure of our society – our cities, our schools, our roads and our hospitals. We need it, thirdly, to enable us to play our part in meeting the challenge of poverty in the world beyond our shores. We need it again to enable our country to hold its own in the great power struggles of the globe, struggles out of which only a few fortunate, or poor and unimportant, nations can contract. And there is perhaps a fifth reason: we need it to maintain our national self-respect, our dynamic as a people.

Growth therefore is of paramount importance. But it is important also in a more immediate, parochial way. I believe – and I will demonstrate the arguments for this belief in the course of this book – that a climate of steady expansion, without inflationary pressures or sharp fluctuations in demand, provides the best conditions for innovation, for the improvement of business efficiency, and for the dissolution of conflict between management and labour; it is in these conditions that change becomes most acceptable and most profitable. For this reason too, therefore, sustained economic growth is – to say the least – an objective not lightly to be discarded.

But if the demand for labour is to be kept down and production is simultaneously to be pushed up, and there are no large reserves of labour available, what is the solution? The answer – and it is an answer on which the future not only of the British but of many other economies is going to depend – is by increasing productivity, by using existing manpower resources far more efficiently than we have done so far. This was the lesson which emerged from the Neddy Council meeting of 4 December 1963. It is a lesson which is going to be with us, in one way or another, throughout the sixties.

And not only in Britain. In retrospect, it is clear that Europe's Age of Miracles – and I propose to tamper somewhat with the rules of geography and assign Japan a position somewhere on the European periphery – depended largely on two factors: on a vast unsatisfied demand for mass consumer goods (especially durables), and on a large pool of relatively highly skilled, relatively cheap labour. As we have seen, neither of these existed to anything like the same extent in the United States. The second existed to a much greater extent in some European countries than in others – in West Germany, Italy and Japan for example much more than in Britain or the Scandinavian countries – and this difference goes a long way, though not the whole way, towards explaining the varied performance of the different European economies. The question is how far these special factors are going to continue to operate through the sixties. The menace of consumer saturation has begun to loom larger in the more affluent European economies, and it is clear that a bigger sales effort is required in the sixties than in the fifties to find markets for all the products of Europe's consumer goods industries.

If the evidence on consumer saturation is somewhat inconclusive, that on the price and availability of labour is indisputable. The reserves of manpower which gave some of the Continental economies their special edge in the fifties have virtually disappeared, and the cost of Continental labour has risen correspondingly. Inflationary pressures generated by union wage demands have emerged in the last few years in Germany (where they have on the whole been contained with considerable success), France and Italy (where they have not). The problems with which the British have been wrestling virtually since the war – problems of wage inflation and intermittent labour shortage – have become, in the last few years, relevant to the whole of Europe. If I concentrate my examination in the next few pages on the problems of Britain, therefore, it is not because our problems are unique – it is precisely because they are typical.

### The Use and Abuse of Labour

On 1 March 1964 an American consultant, Mr William W. Allen, published an article in the *Sunday Times* which attracted a good deal of justifiable attention. Mr Allen posed the question: 'Is Britain a half-time country, getting half-pay for half-work under half-hearted management?' He stated:

For every person required to produce a ton of steel in America, three are required in Britain. By a similar method of comparison, the ratio in aluminium is one to two point five. In the maintenance engineering activities of the two chemical industries, the ratio is about one to four. (In each of these examples, the technologies employed by the industries of each country are at approximately the same levels.)

Mr Allen went on:

In shipbuilding . . . ships could be constructed with about 40 per cent fewer men if labour were employed efficiently. This could be achieved . . . simply by removing the more irrational and non-logical forms of demarcation practised by labour and management alike. . . . It takes three to six times as long to build a house in Britain as it does in America. Two to three times as much time is required in Britain to build a block of flats or an office block. The sales prices of houses (per square foot) in Britain are only slightly lower than they are in America, even though the wages of the construction workers in the latter country are about three times higher than in the former.

Mr Allen could be expected to know what he was talking about. A consultant with many years' experience of British industry, he had engineered the Fawley productivity agreements which pioneered a new type of labour contract in Britain. In 1958, Esso (the British subsidiary of Standard Oil, New Jersey) wanted to expand operations at its Fawley refinery in Southampton Water. At that time its work force was already twice as large as that found in comparable North American refineries, and if it had carried out its planned recruiting programme it would have been three times as great. Instead, a new labour contract was negotiated with the local trade unions in which the management in effect 'bought the union rule book', bargaining drama-tic wage increases, improved conditions and guaranteed job security against higher productivity and the abandonment of institutional barriers to labour flexibility. As a result of the agreement worked out by Allen and his colleagues, Fawley was able to carry out its £23 million expansion plan with a modest net *reduction* in its labour force. The trend towards 'productivity bargaining' on the Fawley principle was subsequently taken up by a number of other British concerns – including most of the other big oil companies, I.C.I., Steel Company of Wales, Pressed Steel, International Publishing Corporation, Electricity Council, and the nationalized airlines.

There was another reason for taking Allen's figures seriously – the fact that in a sense they were not new. They merely reinforced and brought up to date the findings of the Anglo-American Productivity Teams which toured U.S. and British industry in the early post-war years. Then, as now, remarkable differences had been discovered in the typical manning scales of the two countries – differences reflected in relative wage levels.

The depressing feature of Allen's findings was how little improvement there had been in Britain's relative performance since then.

Allen concluded:

1. There is no shortage of labour.
2. Britain has not enjoyed a condition of full employment since 1946.
3. Virtually every employee in British industry is under-employed.
4. Basic wages and salaries are too low.
5. The length of the normal week is too long.
6. Overtime, which is now being worked by male employees, on average, at the rate of 12 to 14 per cent per annum, is unnecessary.
7. Relative to the available manpower, there is an insufficient supply of capital equipment.
8. Nevertheless, the existing capital equipment is under-employed because of the extensive under-employment of labour.
9. The National Economic Development Council and the present Government are not correct when they say that the appropriate growth rate for the British economy is 4 per cent per annum.

In fact, he argued, Britain's existing gross national product could be produced with about half the current work force, working a normal work week of 35 to 40 hours with 2 to 3 per cent overtime – given, that is, more efficient management, more flexible labour, and a more rapid and widespread application of modern technology. Allen claimed that this could be achieved in ten to fifteen years, and that the Neddy growth target should therefore be stepped up to between 8 and 12 per cent per annum. He recognized that this would require changes in national psychology and social attitudes, as well as institutional changes; we shall deal with these later in the book. But he was confident that it could be done.

When one looks at America, one sees why. At the time when Allen's article appeared, U.S. industrial production had risen from its low point at the end of 1960 by over 20 per cent – or by rather more than the *whole* British annual output. But this unprecedented jump in production had been achieved without making any serious inroads into the country's reserve of un- employed manpower. The unemployment rate at the end of 1960 was 7 per cent. Four years later it was still 5 per cent. To a limited extent this discrepancy reflected the rise in the working popula- tion. More jobs were created by the industrial boom, but little more than enough to offset the increase in the number of school leavers seeking jobs. The dramatic fact, however, was the extent to which the increase in production came from higher pro- ductivity on the part of the existing work force – reflecting, mainly, the extension of automation.[6] Since 1964 this trend has continued still further. By August 1965 production had risen a further 10 per cent and unemployment still stood at $4\frac{1}{2}$ per cent. It was not until the end of 1965 – when the boom was five years old and the production index was 35 per cent above 1960 – that unemployment dropped to 4 per cent and labour shortages began to appear on a significant scale.

The British experience was somewhat different. British out- put rose by some 12 per cent between the recession year of 1962 and the boom year of 1964. This expansion had already, by early 1964, begun to run up against labour bottlenecks which were to become increasingly acute in 1965 (when output went up by a further $2\frac{1}{2}$ per cent) and early 1966. As a consequence the rise in wages and prices in the United Kingdom between 1962 and 1965 averaged 5 per cent and $3\frac{1}{2}$ per cent respectively per annum. In the United States, on the other hand, between 1960 and 1965 the annual average increase in hourly earnings was just over 3 per cent and in prices just over 1 per cent. To put the same point in another way: between 1962 and 1965 labour costs per unit of output in the United Kingdom went up by 1 per cent per annum; in the United States between 1960 and 1965 they fell by 1 per cent per annum.

The contrast is startling. In the United States, where auto-mation had been displacing an estimated 40,000 jobs a week, unemployment had remained an obstinate social, economic and political problem. But at the same time it had been an enormous source of strength, for it had given America the leeway – even after a boom unprecedented both in duration and intensity – for further expansion, without running into the bottlenecks which, as we have seen, have continued to impede British efforts to achieve the same sort of growth. The economic miracle to date of the sixties has been America's. In Britain, by contrast, the experience of the Labour administration in its first two years of office has shown, only too clearly, the structural straitjacket in which the economy is enclosed. Despite all the measures which have been taken to improve the working of the economy – which will be dealt with in later chapters – the salient facts remain that the Labour government has been forced, even more sharply than its Conservative predecessors, to apply restraints to growth at a time when the economy was still growing appreciably more slowly than most of our main competitors.

This is our basic problem. Unless we (and 'we' in this context means Europe as well as Britain) can start to adopt U.S. standards of technology, automation and labour utilization, it is hard to see how we are going to match U.S. growth rates. We are losing, if we have not already lost, our great traditional advantage *vis-à-vis* the United States of cheap and plentiful skilled labour. From now on, therefore, we are going to have to use it as skilfully and efficiently as U.S. industry has learned to use *its* labour – with the tenderness of a very scarce resource. American industry has traditionally been forced to do this by the high cost, rather than the natural scarcity, of its work force. The consequences of its adaptation to this situation, as we shall see in Chapter 3, are in some ways bizarre and paradoxical. On this side of the Atlantic we have traditionally used our labour much more wastefully. This can no longer continue – not because British or European labour yet costs as much as American, but because of its growing scarcity in relation to demand.

We have talked a great deal in Britain about the challenge and the opportunity of automation.[6] Before he became Prime Minister, Mr Harold Wilson used to like to make our flesh creep by warning that over the next ten years Britain would need to find something like ten million new jobs (out of a total labour force of some 24 million) to replace those liable to be lost through automation. But in fact the startling thing about automation in Britain so far has been the length of time it has taken to arrive (under Mr Wilson's administration as under his predecessors'). According to a report presented to an automation conference under the auspices of the International Institute of Labour Studies in Geneva, 1964, the United Kingdom had 26 computers installed, or on order, per million of the industrial working population at the end of 1961. The comparative figures for Belgium and West Germany were 36; France 37; Netherlands 34; and Italy 24; making an average for the Common Market countries of 33. Switzerland had 68 per million, the United States 240. Other figures circulated during the 1964 election suggested that the United Kingdom had actually dropped behind all the six Common Market countries (Luxembourg excluded)

and all the European Free Trade Association (E.F.T.A.) countries except Austria and Portugal in computer installation per
capita, and that the French and German ratios were running at
about twice the British. Yet in the late 1950s Britain had the
highest per capita computer population in Europe. (It is fair to
say that all statistics of computer installations are subject to a
wide margin of error, depending partly on definitions; and that
there is a good deal of evidence to suggest a fairly marked
acceleration in computer orders by British industry in the last
two or three years. It is also fair to say that in all countries much
money has been wasted through the misuse of computers, and
that improvement comes not just from installing computers but
from using them effectively after installation.)

Another important index of technological advance is the use
of numerical control. In 1965, according to Sir John Toothill of
Ferranti (the country's leading producer of numerically controlled machine tools), the total amount of numerical control
installed in British industry saved about 700 jobs. Yet in the
engineering industry alone there was a potential saving of
250,000 or so jobs by the introduction of numerical control.
There is a good deal of evidence from other sources that, despite
recent improvements, the United Kingdom has been lagging
behind most of her Continental competitors (not excluding the
Soviet Union) in the installation of automatic process control
systems. We seem, in short, to have been less successful than
many of our neighbours in Europe in adapting ourselves to the
need to adopt transatlanic standards and techniques. (What is
being done to meet this challenge is described in Chapter 5.)

The same picture emerges if we look at automation in its
looser and broader – and economically more meaningful – sense,
in the displacement of labour by advanced forms of capital
equipment. At the beginning of 1963 there appeared to be substantial excess capacity in British industry as a result of the
combination of a capital investment boom with a stagnant
demand for consumer goods over the preceding three years.

While this investment did allow a significant increase in production to take place over the three following years, I think it is true to say that the margin was smaller than might have been expected. In too many cases the investment produced disappointingly little by way of increased productivity – though in others, where the investment was accompanied by good management, the results were highly gratifying.

## Westward, Look!

What is the conclusion? America's today is our tomorrow. Europe's Age of Miracles of the fifties is over, and a new sort of miracle – of technological innovation and managerial wizardry – is needed for the late-sixties and seventies. That this type of miracle is not impossible for Europe is shown by, among other things, the impressive performance of the West German economy in the last few years, in a situation of even greater labour tightness than Britain's. It is indeed possible that Germany will be Europe's trail-blazer in the second post-war *Wirtschaftswunder* as she was in the first.

To draw the relevant lessons we must look more closely at what has been happening in and to U.S. business in the last few years, for this is the economic milieu which is starting to obtain on this side of the Atlantic too. In this chapter I have concentrated rather heavily on one aspect – the use of labour. Of equal importance is the application of science and technology to the industrial process. And in each case the crucial factor is the quality and performance of management. We shall be looking, in later chapters, at what the Labour government has been trying to do to grapple with Britain's problems as described in this chapter, and at what more needs to be done – by government, by industry, by trade unions, by educators and consumers. But before doing so we need to look more closely at the U.S. scene, and particularly at what has been happening in the crucial areas – automation, management, research and development – which go to make up the general climate of innovation and change in which we have most to learn from America. Then we can see how far America's experience applies to us.

NOTES TO CHAPTER ONE

1. See *The Management of the British Economy 1945–60* by J. C. R. Dow (Cambridge University Press, 1964).

2. See *Sunshades in October* by Norman Macrae (Allen & Unwin, 1963).

3. An example of the waste of money which can be involved in an investment programme carried out without any realistic product or market research is the British Railways modernization programme launched in 1955. Other obvious examples occur in the field of defence and aviation.

4. Both reports are obtainable from H.M. Stationery Office.

5. Of course profits could be affected by other factors – changes in raw-material prices for example, or in government taxation. But these would not necessarily be affected one way or the other by movements in the wage bill, and are not therefore directly relevant to this discussion.

6. 'Automation' is a difficult word, meaning different things to different people. One can distinguish three main types of automation, though in practice they are not necessarily easily separable:

(a) *Advanced mechanization*, or *Detroit automation*, where manufacturing operations are linked together in lines of continuous production down which the product moves untouched by hand;

(b) *Numerical and automatic control*, for example where the operation of a machine tool is controlled by instructions on tape or punched card, or by electronic devices which maintain set standards of quality or accuracy by feedback control – that is, by continuously adjusting the controls according to the output;

(c) *Electronic data processing*, the automatic handling of information by electronic computers.

To confuse things still further, the United States authorities tend to define automation as any technological innovation which displaces labour – whereas 'pure' automation in the sense of automatic (normally computer-directed) process controls may on balance create more jobs than it destroys. It is the broader, U.S. definition that is employed in this book. Even in this sense, of course, automation may in the long run prove a net job-creator, just as mechanization did in the first Industrial Revolution. But its initial effect, as with mechanization, is likely to be otherwise.

# CHAPTER TWO

# THE UNITED STATES –
# CHALLENGE AND RESPONSE

UNITED STATES industry in the fifties faced two great challenges which, as we have seen, applied far less urgently to Europe. The first was the high cost of labour – between two and three times as high as America's overseas competitors. The second was the recalcitrance of the consumer, and the intensely competitive atmosphere this engendered. The response to this challenge was threefold. First, there was rapid growth in research and development, primarily to develop new products but also to make existing products cheaper or better or simply 'different'. This development went hand in hand with a growth in marketing techniques and methods of all kinds. Second, and again in the field of technology, there was a remarkable growth in the techniques and application of automation, in the broad sense of the substitution of sophisticated capital equipment for labour. Third, in order to cope with the rapidly changing technological and market environment there was a great upsurge of interest in the techniques of management.

In the next two chapters I propose to look at each of these developments in turn, and to try to examine how far they have gone to solve America's problems, and how far they have in fact thrown up new ones. Let us look first at what has been called in the United States the 'research revolution'.

Between 1957 and 1964 the number of American scientists and engineers employed full-time on research and development (or 'R. & D.' as it is commonly called) almost doubled and total expenditure on R. & D. rose by well over 50 per cent to some $20,000 million (approaching £6,000 million). Of this $14,000 million was spent by the Federal Government ($9,000 million being used for projects carried out in industrial organizations), $5,500 million was spent by industry, and the balance by universities and institutions. (The estimated Federal contribution for 1967 is around $17,000 million). Federal expenditure on R. & D. has been growing at a rate of 20 per cent per annum since 1950. It is estimated that 3·6 per cent of the entire U.S. labour force, or 2·7 million people, are scientists, engineers, technicians or science teachers, and by 1970 the figure is expected to have reached 4 million or 4·7 per cent of the labour force. Nevertheless, the demand for this type of labour in the U.S. exceeds the supply. Hence the demand for British, Commonwealth and Continental scientists and technologists in the U.S. which has given rise to the phenomenon of the 'brain drain'.

How do these figures compare with those of other countries? The most comprehensive study so far relates to 1962, and is contained in a report for the O.E.C.D. (Organization for Economic Cooperation and Development) on *The Research and Development Effort in Western Europe, North America and the Soviet Union* by C. Freeman and A. Young. According to this study U.S. expenditure on R. & D. averaged 3·1 per cent of total national income, and 6·2 per cent of the population were employed in one form or other of work related to R. & D. By comparison the U.S.S.R. spent $2\frac{1}{2}$–3 per cent of national income on R. & D., and 4·4 per cent of its population were employed on it. Spending in Western Europe was proportionally much less, at 1·6 per cent of national income; and R. & D. work employed only 2·9 per cent of Western Europe's labour force.

Among the Western European countries there were, however, considerable discrepancies. U.K. expenditure on R. & D. amounted to 2·2 per cent of national income, compared to Germany's 1·3 per cent and France's 1·5 per cent.

At official rates of exchange the United States spent four times as much on R. & D. in 1962 as Western Europe, and between three and four times as much as the Soviet Union. If one adjusts for the fact that a given unit of research costs different amounts in different countries, the United States involvement in R. & D. would appear to be about two-and-a-half times the Western European, but only some 20 per cent more than Russia's.

There are, however, significant differences between the distribution and methods of research practised in the different countries. On the manpower side, the ratio of engineers to scientists on R. & D. work is much higher in the United States and Russia than in Western Europe, partly because of the much larger available supply of qualified engineers in these two countries. Moreover, 75 per cent of the United States R. & D. budget in 1962 was spent in the business sector (though most of it, as we have seen, is financed by government), while in Western Europe the proportion falls to 60 per cent. Government institutes carry out a much bigger proportion of R. & D. in Britain and France than elsewhere in Europe, while in the Soviet Union research is mainly carried out in industry-wide research institutes.

Finally, the proportion of R. & D. expenditure going on defence and aerospace projects in 1962 was 60 per cent in the United States, against 40 per cent in the United Kingdom and only 33 per cent for Western Europe as a whole. This means that the ratio of American to Western European R. & D. spending in these sectors was seven to one at official exchange rates, four to one in real terms. Comparable figures for the U.S.S.R. were not available, but the proportion of total R. & D. spent on military and space projects is presumably very large indeed.

These differences help to explain the variations in effectiveness of, and the direction taken by, the research efforts of the different countries in the post-war period. The advantage enjoyed by the United States through the economies of scale due to the size of her economy – and the size of many of the companies with a big R. & D. component – is obviously enormous; but I do not believe it fully explains the huge lead acquired by the United States over Western Europe (and, except for a very few areas, over the U.S.S.R.). I believe we have also to consider the degree of understanding of the nature of the problem, and – perhaps most important of all – the climate within which the researchers work.

One does not have to spend much time in the U.S. business environment to discover the importance which for some years has attached to R. & D., both within the company structure and in determining a company's image outside. The investment analyst – that potent figure in the American business world – is expected to analyse the efficiency of a company's research organization as keenly as the viability of its financial structure or the calibre of its senior executives, when investigating its investment possibilities. And woe betide the American corporation that fails to convince the investor that it is putting a reasonable effort into research! Its shares are unlikely to make much of a showing on Wall Street, no matter how admirable its financing or how reliable its standard products.

There is no doubt that, in its continual search for novelty and excitement, the United States has allowed some of the glamour of the test-tube to go to its head. We shall see some manifestations of this in the pages ahead, and we shall see that the Americans themselves have become conscious of it. But there is no doubt that the basic American instinct for innovation is right. In a world where the forces of change are working as rapidly and forcefully as they are today, there can be no invulnerable standard product lines, no natural monopolies whose position cannot be eroded by a new product, a new technique, a shift in consumer preference. This, as we shall see, is one of the great lessons which American industry has learned, but which is not yet fully understood elsewhere.

This means that there tends to be a closer connexion in America than in Britain between the scientist and the boardroom, and a closer nexus between research and profitability. The research association, linked with a trade association rather than with an individual firm, which plays a major part in the

R. & D. effort in the United Kingdom, is almost totally absent from the United States. Its place tends to be taken by the independent contract research firm, supplementing the 'in-firm' research of corporations and government by carrying out specific assignments for clients on a contract basis. Americans argue, with some justification, that this method of doing research is likely to produce a better commercial pay-off than the kind of work done in a research association laboratory, the fruits of which must be shared out among an entire industry rather than accrue to a single firm.

## Contract Researchers and Others

It may well be worth spending a little time looking at the United States contract research firm, partly because it is virtually unique to North America, partly as a guide to the special *ambience* of the United States 'research revolution'. I shall take as my particular example the firm of Arthur D. Little, not because it is different from the others but largely because it is typical.

First, some statistics. The total turnover of the United States contract research industry is probably in the region of $600–650 million a year. It is divided into two groups – the profit-making and non-profit-making organizations. In the second group come the 'Big Three' – the Stanford Research Institute in California, the Battelle Memorial Institute, and the Illinois Institute of Technology (formerly Armour) Research Institute – with a combined annual turnover in the region of $150 million. Each of these institutes is linked with, but to all intents and purposes distinct from, a university or similar educational institution. Smaller than, but similar to, the Big Three are six smaller outfits with an annual average turnover of around $5 million each. An increasing number of universities have established engineering experimental stations or sponsored research laboratories which take on contract research work as a sideline, and in many cases these institutions now have an annual turnover of $2 million or more. (The total number of research laboratories in the United States is estimated to have risen from 290 to 5420 between 1920 and 1960.) Finally, individual university staff members do research for industry or the government on a freelance basis, the collective value of which is quite large. (This classification excludes two very important contract research centres where work is primarily government-oriented – the Rand Corporation and the Massachusetts Institute of Technology's M.I.T.R.E.).

On the profit-making side of the industry, there is one large firm, Arthur D. Little Inc., whose operations are on about the same scale as Armour, Battelle or Stanford; and a very wide range of much smaller, and usually highly specialized, independent laboratories, consultants and engineering design companies. Increasingly, too, as we shall see, there is an overlap between the contract research firms and the big management consultants (of whom more later) like Booz, Allen or McKinsey, and also the management accountants.

Of all these firms the pioneer is Arthur D. Little – 'A.D.L.' – which started as a two-man chemical laboratory back in the 1880s and today has a payroll of over 1,400, more than half of them professionally qualified and a substantial proportion sporting Ph. D.s. Little claims to have been the first commercial organization in the world to engage primarily in contract research on technical processes, and today the range of inquiry which it handles is bewildering. Its inventions include instant breakfast foods and missile fuels, hot-drink paper cups and low-temperature cryostats, nylon fishing lines and atomic-fallout filters. From the 'bread-and-butter' scientific research work with which it made its name it has branched out into such fields as product development, operational research, technical audits, management consultancy, regional development, urban renewal, engineering and automation work, marketing – almost anything in fact which has a research content and in which one or more members of the staff are interested.

This second qualification is more important than it sounds.

for one thing on which A.D.L. does not seem to have done any research or planning is its own development. Its expansion has been positively Topsy-like, largely because – at least so far as I could discover on a visit to the company headquarters at Acorn Park, near Cambridge, Mass. – nobody ever appears to give orders to anybody at Little. The atmosphere is more academic than industrial, and while there is an organization structure on paper it doesn't really mean much in practice. The climate is about as fluid, permissive and anti-authoritarian as it could well be in a commercial organization. This means that when an inquiry comes in – and these can run the whole gamut from: 'I want to diversify. Can you develop a product for me?' to 'My research department doesn't seem to be achieving anything; is it my fault or theirs?', or 'We are a new country; can you draw up an economic plan for us?' – it is passed to the man who is considered most expert in this particular subject, who may in fact be quite junior. If he decides to take it on, and if the central contracting people at Little can agree terms with the clients, he then sets out to recruit a team from within the organization to tackle it.

Seniority hardly comes into this at all. The team leader on one project may have people working under him who are much more senior than he is. The team leader on one project may be working under a member of his team on another one. The crucial point – and this is really the lesson which the contract research industry has to teach – is that successful research into business problems requires two things: the right atmosphere, and a blending of different disciplines. A.D.L.'s critics argue that democracy (helped by the fact that it is wholly owned by its own Pension Fund) has sometimes got in the way of growth. Whether or not this has been true in the past – and Little's growth rate is in fact one that most companies would envy – it does not seem to be now.

## Some Techniques: Operational Research

The fact is that the research problems of modern industry typically require a mixing of different disciplines, and it is this which a contract research organization like A.D.L. or the Big Three can provide. Take for example operational research, which in recent years has succeeded product development as perhaps the biggest growth sector, not only in A.D.L. but also in the whole U.S. contract research industry (though some would argue that other management techniques — not necessarily mathematical in nature — are ahead). Operational research involves the application of the principles and methods of science to problems of strategy.[1] It is a technique for reducing the chaos and complexity of business operations — what Lord Heyworth, when chairman of Unilever, once described as the 'creative fog' of management decision — to the simplicity of the laboratory or control panel, essentially through the application of statistics. (This does not mean, of course, that O.R. solves management problems in the sense of removing the need for decisions. What it does is to provide clear-cut alternatives for decisions — so that these can be based on rational judgement rather than hunch or intuition.) Originally pioneered by the British in the Second World War, to provide guide-lines for solving the logistic and strategic problems of the allied forces in the Battle of the Atlantic and the invasion of Western Europe, it was subsequently largely taken over by Americans as an industrial and commercial tool — probably the most basic and fundamental of all the tools of management which we shall be discussing in this book.

The point to be stressed here, however, is that 'O.R. men' typically operate in teams, using the common language of mathematics, but — in the best cases, at least — embracing graduates of such diverse disciplines as economics, engineering, physics, statistics, social and behavioural sciences, etc., in order to bring as many approaches as possible to bear on a single problem. Successful operational research therefore involves the crossing and blending of different disciplines on a scale which cuts right across the traditional specialisms of the academic world. 'In this business we're always finding ourselves crossing intellectual frontiers,' one of the top men at A.D.L. says.

The development of the computer as a calculating tool in recent years has given operational research an enormous fillip, and carried it into new worlds of application. Originally based on industrial engineering, where it moved into the gap left between the accountants, the industrial engineers and the quality control people, it has tended increasingly to infiltrate into broader fields of industrial economics and beyond. It has also, uniquely among the new business disciplines, given rise to a science all its own – the study of Cybernetics, which deals with communication and control as applied by animal (including human) organisms, social groups and communities (including, of course, factories) and machines. One of the main objects of cybernetics is to develop machines with the same kind of communication and control characteristics as animal (including human) brains and nervous systems – mainly via the analogue computer. Cybernetics therefore plays a seminal role in the development of automation, primarily by designing machines with the capacity to absorb information and, by feed-back, to correct themselves accordingly. The self-correcting machine is, of course, the basic element of automatic process control, since it removes the need for any human intervention or control.

Cybernetics clearly breaches the traditional frontiers of academic disciplines on a major scale. The cybernetician, says Gordon Pask, one of this country's leading exponents, 'can legitimately examine such diverse assemblies as genes in a chromosome, the contents of books in a library (with respect to information storage), ideas in brains, government and computing machines (with respect to the learning process)'.[2] He is concerned with the common functional characteristics of all control systems, and an organism is after all a species of control system.

Some typical examples of O.R. assignments carried out by A.D.L. may help to illustrate the type of problem tackled. An insurance company suspected some of its adjusters were working in collusion with claimants. A.D.L. was asked to apply statistical checks to see whether these suspicions were *a priori* justified – a fairly straightforward application of one of the basic statistical tools of operational research, namely Probability Theory.

Another example illustrates the application of Queueing Theory, which deals with the flow of people or goods through service points and the ways of avoiding delays and bottlenecks, and eliminating unnecessary waiting time. American Airlines wanted advice on whether, and if so how, to automate its reservation system. A similar case arose over the U.S. Air Force's plan to automate its cargo-handling system – a project involving demand and logistic studies also. A typical British Queueing-Theory case in recent years was the Post Office's decision, based on a study by Associated Industrial Consultants, to make its counters all multi-purpose.

Queueing-Theory problems arise in one form or another in almost all service facilities – particularly in retail stores and transport undertakings. Their relevance, for example, in road planning and traffic engineering, in air-traffic control and port operations is fairly obvious. But the scope is broader than this, for queues can consist of materials as well as people. Inventory control, and ensuring an adequate flow of materials, parts and components to a fast-moving assembly line, are obvious cases in point. Indeed, one of the great successes of U.S. computer operations in the last few years has been in the field of stock control. This, perhaps more than anything else, stopped the United States boom at its peak in 1964 from going the way of all previous booms and degenerating into inflation through speculative stockpiling.

Similar O.R. techniques have recently been used by some of the largest distributive organizations in the United Kingdom to study and rationalize their physical distribution systems – to achieve economies and greater efficiency in the flow of goods from factory via warehouse and retail outlet to the customer. In some cases this exercise is resulting in a radical reorganization of the grouping and structure of depots and warehouses.

Short-term linear programming work in such areas as inventories, production planning and marketing operations has made up the bulk of operational research work in industry on both sides of the Atlantic. But the growth areas of the future are likely to lie increasingly in the field of long-term planning and investment and overall business strategy. Capital replacement, industrial location and resource allocation are obvious fields for application of O.R. methods. National economic planning through the development of econometric models is a field where useful work has been done in the United States, Britain and the Netherlands in particular, but where much more could, and needs to, be done. (Important use was made of the Department of Applied Economics' computer-based Social Accounting Matrix at Cambridge, U.K., in working out the British 1970 National Economic Plan.) Urban renewal and regional development are also cases in point. In both Britain and America there is an urgent need to educate more town planners in the potential of operational research. In the U.S. operational research has been used in long-term collective bargaining. The break-through here came in the 1960 Fawley-type agreement with the International Longshoremen of the U.S. West Coast ports, where union opposition to automation was bought off by job security and pension guarantees – after a detailed actuarial study had convinced the employers that the dockers' age-structure was such as to provide scope for a mutually profitable agreement!

Another major field of operational research is in strategy – both in defence and business. Here the key concept is the Theory of Games, widely employed in strategic studies, in the evolution of the Business Games now taught to aspiring executives, and in the more sophisticated market studies carried out by some of the leading companies. Allied to this is the work being done on

Decision Theory, which seeks to analyse the decision-making functions of the various levels of management, and to enable top management to isolate the handful of critical or controlling factors in any given situation on which its own decision-making should be concentrated – to provide, as it were, beacons in Lord Heyworth's all-enveloping managerial fog (or, to use another terminology, to alleviate the manager's existential *Angst*).

An example of Decision Theory technique is the Decision-Tree concept adapted from French models by A.D.L.'s John Magee – a kind of do-it-yourself executive kit for resolving investment decisions, using 'an intimate combination of techniques such as discounted cash flow with marketing research, O.R. and engineering analysis to help management reach a decision based on clearer understanding of its motives, alternatives and risks.'[3] This process, says Magee, 'does not eliminate risk but identifies its nature'.

The Decision-Tree concept sets out to identify the nature and extent of uncertainty surrounding a project – is it statistical in character, is it avoidable or insurable in whole or in part, and what is the nature of the risk it generates? – and to assess the possible consequential damage to the decision-makers if the risks eventuate; it seeks also to evaluate the possible costs and returns of the investment, and therefore the relative value of alternative outcomes. An example of a Decision-Tree chart for a fairly simple decision – whether or not to authorize a new project – is given below. It will be seen that each decision calls forth a sequence of events which will in turn require subsequent decisions. There is, of course, no magic in this technique. It will not *by itself* solve any problems, but it should make them easier to solve if properly applied. (Improperly applied, without the saving grace of common sense, it could be disastrous.) The main point, however, is its educative effect. An executive who habitually approaches problems in this sort of way, by using this kind of discipline and expecting his colleagues to do likewise, is going to create a different sort of organization and to follow a different sort of policy from one who proceeds by intuition or by counting heads. What we have here is the difference between the professional and the amateur, and it is a difference to which we shall return more than once in this book. Concepts like the Decision Tree are part of the tool-bag of the professional manager, and what they make of him is probably as important as what he makes of them.

## Some Techniques: Network Analysis

The Decision-Tree chart overleaf is what is technically known as a 'network'. But it is a particular, rather simple, type of network. Network Analysis is commonly used for the programming of construction jobs, for solving the sort of problems thrown up by Queueing Theory, ensuring that the various stages of the work are brought forward in correct sequence, with the least delay and the least cost. With construction industries under pressure in most countries – including, until very recently, Britain – the role of Network Analysis is particularly topical. (It is worth noting that of the seven years it takes to build a new hospital, for example, in Britain today, only two years consists of actual construction, the rest is spent planning.)

Network Analysis of a sort has been known since the First World War, when the U.S. Army Ordnance Bureau invented the Gantt or bar chart as a means of checking on the progress of munitions supply orders. The next step forward was the flow process chart, which provides a graphic representation of the order in which operations have to be performed to accomplish a project. Both these methods provide a rough means of checking whether work is going forward on schedule, and at what stage the different sequences need to be performed. But neither is particularly good at spotting the key bottlenecks which are liable to hold up the whole operation. This is better done by a newer technique, the Line of Balance (L.O.B.), developed out of a combination of the Gantt and flow process charts; this is

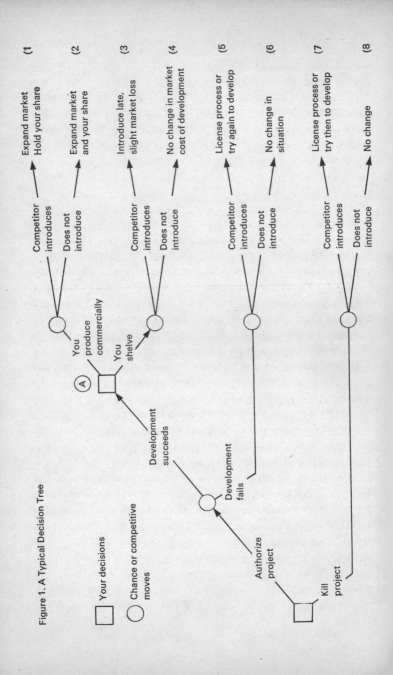

Figure 1. A Typical Decision Tree

Your decisions

Chance or competitive moves

Development succeeds

Authorize project

Kill project

Development fails

You produce commercially

You shelve

Competitor introduces — Expand market
Does not introduce — Hold your share   (1

Competitor introduces — Expand market
Does not introduce — and your share   (2

Competitor introduces — Introduce late,
Does not introduce — slight market loss   (3

No change in market
cost of development   (4

Competitor introduces — License process or
Does not introduce — try again to develop   (5

No change in
situation   (6

Competitor introduces — License process or
Does not introduce — try then to develop   (7

No change   (8

designed to show the relationship between actual progress and delivery commitments and to pinpoint bottlenecks.

These are all, however, fairly rough-and-ready techniques. Of a higher order of sophistication altogether are the two most currently favoured types of Network Analysis, Critical Path and P.E.R.T. (Programme Evaluation and Research Technique). Both evolved independently (a third, similar, variant is 'R.A.M.P.S.', standing for 'Resource Allocation and Multi-Project Scheduling'), in the United States at the end of the fifties. Critical Path Analysis was invented by Du Pont and Remington Rand as an aid to planning, scheduling and co-ordinating new plant construction. Meanwhile the U.S. Navy's Special Project Office was worrying about its Polaris crash-building programme, which was in danger of slipping behind schedule. To meet this problem it devised its own scheduling system known as P.E.R.T., which proved so successful that the Polaris was delivered ahead of time; since then the United States Defense Department has insisted that P.E.R.T. charts should be used on all major development programmes.

These two systems – the differences between them are too subtle to merit discussion here – crossed the Atlantic around 1961 and have since enjoyed a growing vogue in the British construction industry; Costains the builders have been among the British pioneers. The basic idea behind Network Analysis is simple; it involves putting down on paper the necessary sequence of events to be performed in logical order, the resulting chart being known as the 'Network'. An example for a building operation is given below.

The chart consists of a series of activities, or events, joined together by lines or arrows indicating the sequence, with an estimated time-allowance for each. The arrows will fan out from the initial order or decision, and will come together again at the completion of the task. The chart can be analysed by adding up the estimated times along each of many paths from beginning to end of the job. One of these will be longer than

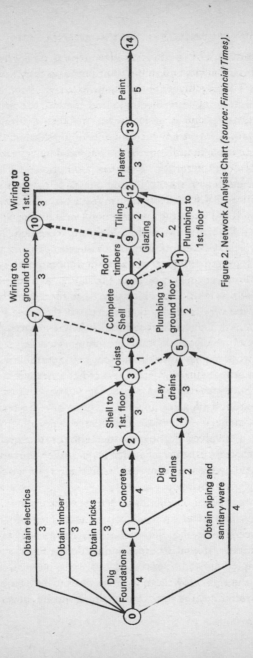

Figure 2. Network Analysis Chart (source: Financial Times).

any of the others. This is the so-called critical path, the one along which bottlenecks are likely to occur, and therefore the one on which management should concentrate.

Network construction is an intellectual exercise of considerable sophistication, and it is clearly a useful mental discipline apart from any other merits it may have. Though the concept may be simple enough, in all but the simplest building operations the application can be highly complex, involving use of computers and careful assessment of the input data. Some experts argue that both P.E.R.T. and Critical Path err in putting too great an emphasis on cutting construction time and not enough on achieving the cheapest and most efficient resource allocation. 'P.E.R.T.', one British authority once told me, 'replaces disorderly allocation of resources by an orderly misallocation.' A good deal of work is now going on – not least in the British Ministry of Public Building and Works – to meet these criticisms and to find new applications for Network Analysis. These include its use to assess the merits of different industrialized building systems, to gauge their various management requirements, to assess the optimum costs for each type of building operation and to establish a basis for programming future work. (This is clearly of enormous importance to the government, for about a half of all building work in Britain today takes place in the public sector.)

A good deal still needs to be done to simplify the actual construction of networks, which can consume much managerial time. Many business concerns are reluctant to go to the trouble of constructing a new network for each individual contract. Much time and trouble can be saved by use of a standard construction sequence, on which can be superimposed the particular characteristics of the job in question. Given continuity of orders, the same network can be used for a complete building programme, thus avoiding the need to design a different one for each single contract. 'Packaged networks' of this kind are increasingly being used by big firms with large and recurring construction needs, like I.C.I. (We shall return to this question of standardization and continuity in programming when we look a little more closely at the problems of building technology in a later chapter.)

Network Analysis has other identical advantages – as a learning tool, as a means of identifying people in the firm with the operation (the best networks, say the experts, like the best economic plans are group productions rather than the inspirations of single minds), and as a way of achieving the same sort of centralized overall management control in a building operation as one gets in a factory – getting away, in fact, from the 'sub-contracting management' mentality where each group of workers (bricklayers, electricians, glaziers, plumbers) has its own separate management. As we shall see, Network Analysis and industrialized building go hand in hand, the one requiring and facilitating the other. But Network Analysis is not confined to construction. It can be used, as the Decision-Tree concept shows, for almost any project involving management decision and spread over a finite time. It is becoming an increasingly important and flexible – though inevitably imperfect – management tool.

An example of the range of Network Analysis for a large business enterprise was given in the Unilever magazine *Progress* in the third quarter of 1964. An article by L. J. Rawle, entitled 'The Right Order of Things', describes Unilever's experience of Network Analysis. 'Among the many Unilever projects currently being networked', writes Rawle,

are the setting up of a textile factory in Nigeria, the integration of the Premier supermarket business with Mac Fisheries, the design and construction of palm oil mills in Borneo and the Cameroons, a new accelerated freeze drying plant at Aberdeen, moving a glue factory from one site to another, installing a new computer system, and numerous plant installations. The impact of networks on marketing has been no less dramatic and they are fast becoming standard practice for planning and effecting programmes for the development and launching of food, toilet and soap products, even as far afield as the Philippines. One of the first marketing projects to be planned and completed with the aid of networks was the launching of 'Square Deal Quix' washing-up liquid by Lever Brothers & Associates.

Rawle estimates that

As a general rule about 10 to 15 per cent of the activities [in the average network] are critical and a further 10 to 15 per cent are sub-critical, that is they can easily become critical as a result of a slight delay, or if we re-arrange the plan in any way. The remaining 70 to 80 per cent of activities are found to have 'float' of varying amounts. This is important to management since attention can be concentrated on a minor part of the project, knowing there is sufficient elbow room in the rest of the project for it not to influence the whole pattern of events. . . . While it is feasible to analyse by hand networks comprising as many as six hundred activities, it has usually been found worthwhile to use a computer to do the arithmetic when the number of activities exceeds two hundred.

The article concludes:

Networks are likely to prove of value in any project which is *complex*, in that it has many interdependent activities; or *large*, both in the sense of people involved as well as money and materials; or has to be completed within *stipulated time*, or *cost limits*.

Some British engineering and machine-tool companies – Rolls-Royce, for example – use Network Analysis techniques in their engineering shops to help them meet tight delivery schedules. The network helps them to decide in these circumstances which jobs should have priority on machines.

There, for the moment, we leave the new business techniques. We will be discussing others in later chapters. One factor is shared by them all. They are aids to executive decision-making. In no case do they eliminate the need for decisions. They simply help the executive to make better ones. They do not make him redundant – only more effective.

## The Revolt Against the Scientist

In our study of business techniques, we have moved some way from the affairs of Arthur D. Little and the contract research industry. But the path we have been following, from relatively simple research questions to increasingly complex management ones, is one along which A.D.L. and the other contract research firms have also found themselves inexorably drawn. This relationship between research and management is the next area for us to explore.

During the middle and late 1950s, as we have seen, the scientist enjoyed immense prestige in American business and society – partly for the economic reasons which we have already investigated, partly also because of the shock administered to the United States' self-esteem and sense of security by the Sputnik and the Soviet space challenge generally. For a number of years the scientist could do no wrong, either in industry or in government. 'Research' and 'innovation' were the great vogue-words in American business, and the vice-president in charge of research and development could usually get what he wanted from his fellow-executives. Congress approved the massive space exploration programme with hardly a murmur.

But a reaction set in – interestingly enough, at almost precisely the time when Mr Harold Wilson swung the British Labour Party, and indirectly the whole British political structure, behind the scientific revolution. The reaction against the scientist in the U.S.A. sprang from a number of causes. Partly it represented a change in corporate philosophy, which has been reflected in the power structure of business. The vogue-word for the last few years in U.S. business has been 'corporate planning'. The reconciliation between planning and science is inevitably a difficult one, because the aim of the planner is to be able to foresee the future and reduce the area of uncertainty – whereas the aim of R. & D., at least in part, is to introduce new elements of uncertainty into the picture through innovation. I remember, years ago, the chief planner in one of the eastern European countries telling me, in a tone of barely concealed irritation: 'The one thing one can't plan ahead for is the creativity of our people. Somebody's always coming up with some new idea or technique which has to be fitted into the plan somehow or other.' The same attitudes, though less crudely expressed, are echoed from time to time in the boardrooms of the great enterprises of the capitalist West. For we have here one of the most fundamental conflicts in the human psyche and in human society – the conflict between Order and Creativity. One suspects, though this is inevitably unprovable, that in the last few years the pendulum in the United States executive suite has swung a little way away from Creativity towards Order.

It has been able to do so, not just because of a change in mental fashions, but because some of the return from the heavy investment in research and technology has been somewhat disappointing. People have come to ask where and when the pay-off is coming, and to remark that the emperor's new clothes have in some cases a distinctly naked look. The big inquest into the R. & D. boom which has been going on in the United States has thrown up a new and fascinating line of work for the consultants like A.D.L. in the so-called 'Technical Audit' – an exercise to evaluate the effectiveness of a client's R. & D. department, and to see how it can be improved; and, incidentally, an attempt to clarify the atmosphere of mystery and uncertainty in which too many of these departments lived during the era of the 'scientists' heyday'.

It emerges that the question of the return on investment in research is essentially a variant of the Two Cultures problem. The success of this investment has tended to be proportional to two related factors – the degree of creativity in the climate of

the corporation, and the extent of liaison and mutual understanding between the R. & D. department and top management.
Research has proved most successful where management has
been most emotionally and intellectually committed to its
success. It has also flourished where there is a certain fluidity and
flexibility in the company structure, which permits the interplay
of personality and ideas, and where management is psychologically ready to alter existing plans and patterns to accommodate
change and innovation.

But these conditions do not always exist. In some companies
the chief executives do not understand the nature of research,
and expect a given, determinate result from a given input; they
assume that investment in research is equivalent to, and should
produce results as quickly and surely as, investment in a new
machine. In some companies the influence of the accountant
overshadows the R. & D. effort. In some cases R. & D. departments have been forbidden to work on anything which cannot be
guaranteed to produce a new commercial product inside two
years.

In other cases, so far from trying to clamp the R. & D.
department too tightly into the production and marketing
structure, management goes to the other extreme and tends to
divorce the research function from the rest of the company.
This often happens where top management lacks technical
expertise, or where there is an underlying reluctance to change
established ways and embark on new, risky, imperfectly understood ventures. There are companies with elaborate research
departments – in some cases functioning at least partly as
company status symbols – where there is virtually no communication with the rest of the company, and where the board of
directors would secretly be somewhat disturbed if the department came up with a project requiring executive action! In a
number of cases consultants have found that they have had to
interpret the work of the R. & D. department to top management and vice versa; often the two have been almost totally

ignorant of what the other is doing. In some cases consultants have been commissioned to solve problems on which, unknown to management, the company's own research teams had already been working, sometimes successfully. Only too often the R. & D. department has not known what to do because it has not been told what areas the company is interested in. In such cases the research men become discouraged and hive off on to research which interests them but which may not fit in at all with the overall strategy of the firm.

The fault may not always lie with management directly – though the ultimate responsibility for failure of course must. (The buck must always stop with the chief executive; that is what he is there for.) But many technologists, in the United States as elsewhere, have difficulty communicating their ideas to non-technical people, and often they lack interest in or understanding of marketing. The line of conflict at board level often runs between R. & D. and marketing, and frequently in such cases the marketing director – who is usually, if he is any good at his job, more than averagely fluent and persuasive – starts with a strong advantage in a sales-oriented society.

In such circumstances the outside consultant, whose experience bridges these two cultures, and whose work involves bringing different disciplines together, can act as a useful catalyst. Of course, there is no guaranteed formula for maximizing the real return on R. & D. investment, and different companies tackle the problem in different ways – some successfully, some less so. Here are two highly successful U.S. science-based concerns, each with international ramifications, discussing their research policy.

*Company 1.* 'Our R. & D. department really grew up as a sort of corporate status symbol. We had a non-technical management, and during the fifties we began to diversify into a number of new lines largely as a result of our R. & D. discoveries. Management wasn't leading, it was following rather confusedly in the wake of R. & D. Now our top management is much more technically-oriented, and the whole organization is working much more as a team, to an overall plan. We're now using P.E.R.T. charts to help us to programme our research work, and we're pre-planning not only our applied research operations but also our basic research. We're not dissipating our efforts the way we used to. We're concentrating our resources, particularly the top scientific manpower which will always be one of our scarcest resources, and we're ensuring that our R. & D. people have permanent access to top management and are fully integrated in the team.'

*Company 2*'s attitude to programming of R. & D. work is radically different. 'One of our most valuable discoveries of recent years had a very long gestation period – so long in fact that at one stage management became discouraged and told the scientists to stop work on it. They went on working on it secretly against the company's orders for two years, and during that time they made the breakthrough which turned it into a commercial proposition. Today it's one of our biggest money-spinners. If they'd obeyed orders the company would be a lot poorer today.' This example of the 'serendipity'[4] approach to research probably represents a minority view in large U.S. industry today.

The success of R. & D. must always be partly dependent on luck, partly on the ability of those in the department, partly on their relations with other departments, but more than anything else it will depend on the overall quality of management and its attitude to change. No organization can ever be sure that it has got the recipe just right, and it must never assume that it has.

The fact is that the combination of competition and technology is making the task of business management in many ways more exacting and challenging than ever before. There was a time when, if one discovered a good new product, one could reasonably hope to be left to develop and exploit it in comparative peace for a while. But this is becoming less and less true. Product innovation is becoming more and more of a necessity in the corporate scene, as the old barriers between products are being eroded and the pace of diversification accelerates. When Du Pont developed nylon during the war it had fifteen years of monopoly profits before it, but when it introduced Delrin in 1960 it was only a year before Celanese had a rival product on the market. Natural textiles are invaded by products from the chemical industry. Paper, plastics, metals, glass, textiles are struggling for the same markets. In some cases companies find themselves forced to move into completely new fields of technology to employ surplus capital, to follow a marketing or technological 'lead', or to avoid damaging competition in a traditional and perhaps declining market.

But product innovation and diversification involve leaps into the unknown, and the strain on executives with substantial resources at risk must not be under-rated. If to this human unwillingness to adventure are added failures of communication and mutual trust and respect between the key sections of the organization, the obstacles to successful change plainly become considerable. Thus the consultant's task is often one of Group Dynamics, of trying to explain one section to another, of attempting to remove inhibitions and suspicions and channel the collective energies of the management group towards change and innovation. The technical audit shades off into a species of group therapy.

## The Future of Management

But, though the consultant can catalyse, advise and encourage, the ultimate responsibility rests with management. And it is, as we have seen, a daunting responsibility. The technological revolution is adding a new dimension to the problems of business management, and to a considerable extent altering the whole nature of the managerial function – on the one hand equipping the manager with new sources of knowledge and expertise, on the other adding new uncertainties and imposing new tests of character.

Sympathy for – and understanding of – R. & D., willingness to embrace change, and ability to persuade one's colleagues to go along are obviously non-measurable attributes, and so is the judgement which alone can make the pursuit of innovation ultimately profitable. This is the modern version of the entrepreneurial 'flair' which is the successful businessman's traditional trait. Yet in a number of ways the manager's job is becoming more quantitative, less qualitative; less of an indefinable art, more of a precise and largely communicable technique. As we shall see later, exactly the same process is at work lower down on the factory floor, as a result of automation. One should not over-state the 'triumph of the technocrat'. There is still a sense in which great managers are born and not made; there is still a sense in which management can only be taught through experience that the most crucial decisions depend on imponderables, on personal judgements, that successful management involves the indefinable qualities of leadership and character. All this is true. But while these are necessary conditions for success they are no longer sufficient ones; and the developments of the last decade have both complicated the manager's job and at the same time provided new tools for the solution of his problems. Character and judgement are not enough. Knowledge also is needed.

And the extent of this knowledge is increasing all the time, at a pace few people appreciate. When business management first came to be studied, at Harvard University half a century ago, there was no body of knowledge to draw upon, and it was therefore necessary to rely on the Case Study method of teaching. The Case Study method has great advantages as a mind-trainer and stimulator, but it is not scientific. It presents students with accounts of actual concrete business situations which have occurred – for example, the I.C.I.–Courtaulds battle at the end of 1962 – and leaves them to draw their own conclusions as to the lessons to be learned. This will always be an invaluable element in the training of businessmen, but the range of knowledge has now greatly broadened. A great deal more is known about business techniques, and a great deal more also about the environment in which business has to operate.

Today, therefore, the curriculum of management education needs to contain at least three basic elements. First, there is the practical element provided by Case Studies. Second, there is what is called 'framework' knowledge – applied economics, sociology, psychology and so on. Third, there are the new management skills and techniques used for planning and control – which are, as Lord Franks points out in his report *British Business Schools*[5] 'basically logical methods of analysing and presenting information for decision. . . . Taken together, they represent a far-reaching extension of the principles of scientific method and quantitative analysis into new fields, and as such they are coming to constitute an important element in the contemporary climate of ideas'. These techniques include such things as operational research, linear programming, resource allocation and strategic and business planning, decision theory and its applications, the use and application of computer techniques. Lord Franks pointed out that these are now established subjects of research and graduate teaching in most major U.S. universities (including Harvard) and in some universities in Western Europe – though not yet on any substantial scale in British universities. Since the Franks Report there has been a significant change. Chairs of Operational Research have been established in more than one new university, and other business techniques have also acquired academic respectability and indeed éclat. The syllabus for the 1967 post-graduate programme at the new London Business School given at the end of this book (see Appendix, p. 277), shows how far we have moved from the 'blood and guts' concept of business management.

It is significant that in the United States the long dispute over business teaching methods between the advocates of the Case Study, represented primarily by the Harvard Business School, and the protagonists of more quantitative disciplines, headed by the graduate business school of the Massachusetts Institute of Technology (M.I.T.) across the Charles River, seems to be coming to an end. The dispute itself represented a facet of the Two Cultures controversy, for Harvard is a liberal arts university and M.I.T. an engineering school, and in each case the business school took on the colouring of the parent institution. Today, however, there is a marked softening on both sides, and a recognition that both elements must be present in any effective system of business education. (It is also relevant in this historic controversy that Harvard Business School has always seen itself as primarily marketing-oriented, M.I.T. as primarily production-oriented. Harvard traditionally puts more emphasis than M.I.T. on individualism and less on teamwork.) The same synthesis is at work in most of the other graduate schools throughout the United States. (It is perhaps worth pausing at this point to note that in the United States, unlike Britain or Western Europe, the universities have always taken the lead in providing business education – partly because in the United States there are much closer links between universities and the business world than is common on this side of the Atlantic. This is a crucial factor in economic development about which we shall have more to say later in this book.)

Not only has there been a great growth in the accumulated corpus of knowledge about business management; there has also been a notable refinement of the tools available. The computer provides for the first time a really effective tool for translating management 'hunches' into precise quantitative calculations on the sort of scale required. As computers become more sophisticated, their impact on the type of management expertise required clearly becomes greater.

Moreover, as industry becomes more capitalized and less labour-intensive, the importance of making the right decisions and the penalties of guessing wrong become progressively greater, and the burden on management therefore increasingly great. As competition becomes more intense, as consumer tastes shift increasingly rapidly and unpredictably, and as the pace of technological advance accelerates, the gains and the hazards increase. In the last resort, labour can be paid off. Capital, once installed, has to be serviced whether there is a demand for the products it is designed to make or not. In these circumstances, the old 'hit-or-miss, by-guess-or-by-God' style of management is increasingly inappropriate.

All these factors have been operative on the American business scene for some years, and they are beginning to apply increasingly in Britain and Europe also. They have the combined effect of making management less of an art and more of a science, less of a craft and more of a technique. They are also raising the general standard of knowledge, education and ability required of the business executive. All this has profound implications for society which we will study later on.

So far our investigation of the American scene has been conducted at the 'micro' level of the individual firm. It is now time to broaden our canvas to take in the 'macro' level of the whole economy, and to bring into focus the element which has so far been missing – the element of the state. This will occupy us in the next chapter.

NOTES TO CHAPTER TWO

1. The approved (by the Operational Research Society of Great Britain) definition of O.R. is as follows: 'Operational research is the attack of modern science on complex problems arising in the direction and management of large systems of men, machines, materials and money in industry, business, government and defence. Its distinctive approach is to develop a scientific model of the system, incorporating measurements of factors such as chance and risk, with which to predict and compare the outcomes of alternative decisions, strategies and controls. The purpose is to help management determine its policy and actions scientifically.' The reader who wishes to be fully informed on operational research and cybernetics should read Stafford Beer's monumental *Decision and Control* (Wiley, 1966), a major work by one of the great practitioners of the art.

2. *An Approach to Cybernetics* (Hutchinson, 1961), p. 16.

3. *The Decision Tree* (Arthur D. Little), p. 2.   The chart on page 56 is taken from this book.

4. Serendipity: 'the faculty of making happy and unexpected discoveries by accident' (Shorter Oxford English Dictionary, 3rd edition).

5. British Institute of Management, p. 9.

# CHAPTER THREE

# THE UNITED STATES –
# A PROBLEM OF BALANCE

BETWEEN 1909 and 1947 the long-term growth of productivity or output per man-hour in U.S. private industry averaged 2 per cent per annum. Since the war the annual rate of increase has been 3 per cent, but this long-term average is made up of two peak periods, immediately after the war and in the last few years, with a longish trough of low productivity increases in the fifties in between. Recently, in fact, the rate of increase in the private sector has been running at $3\frac{1}{2}$ per cent or more a year. Moreover, whereas immediately after the war it was agriculture which was chalking up the biggest productivity gains, today it is manufacturing industry. Productivity is still rising in farming, but it is rising more slowly. In industry, on the other hand, it has been accelerating. For production workers, the rate of increase has been more than 4 per cent a year – a rate unequalled since the hectic boom days of the 1920s.

There is a second peculiar feature about the situation of the last few years. For the first time output per man-hour has started to go up faster than total production. There have been significant reductions in the labour requirements of basic industries like coal-mining, textiles, steel and paper. Ten years ago the steel labour force stood at 544,000. By 1965 it was below 400,000. The introduction of continuous mining machinery has cut the mining labour force required by three quarters since 1947. In copper-mining, lumbering and other trades the picture is the same: more capital equipment, more output, fewer jobs.

## Automation and Unemployment

We have already seen that over the six years from 1960–66 in the United States a production increase of around 35 per cent served only to bring unemployment down from 7 per cent to 4 per cent. It is true that, because of different methods of counting, this is probably equivalent to a British rate of about $2\frac{1}{2}$ per cent. Nevertheless, it is still a disturbingly high rate at the top of a boom of unprecedented length and intensity; and, were it not for the war in Vietnam, it would be significantly higher.

An expansion in the number of jobs is needed, not only to reduce the basic unemployment rate, but also to cater for the school leavers who have been coming on to the U.S. labour market at a rate of $1\frac{1}{2}$ million a year. The long-term prospects are not particularly encouraging. It is noteworthy that after each cycle of the U.S. business economy since the war unemployment has settled at a higher level. Is there any reason to think that the trend is likely to be reversed?

There is no particular mystery as to why American unemployment has remained so high in a period of boom. It is due to the pace of technological advance, leading to much higher rates of productivity and to a much higher ratio of capital per worker. Four years ago it was calculated that in the Lake Charles area of Louisiana, a region where jobs are particularly hard to come by, the amount of capital needed to provide each extra job was over $175,000. In the mid-fifties it had been $75,000. By the 1970s it will probably be of the order of $1 million per job. Automated techniques are increasingly moving out from the pace-setters like aero-space and telecommunications into general industry – into coal-mining and the process industries, and also into less obvious areas such as newspaper production, packaging, component assembly, banking and insurance. The revolt of the U.S. consumer against standardization has meant greater flexibility of production and stricter quality control; this has created a growing demand for numerically controlled machine tools taking instructions from a computer. It is a matter of semantics how much of this technological innovation one dignifies with the title 'automation'. The key statistic is that, other things remaining equal, technological change is likely to go on displacing workers at a rate of around 2 million a year.

The United States has in fact been paying the penalty of its success as a productive machine. The Administration in its approach to the problem has tended to talk with two voices – a 'structural' and a Keynesian voice. Only recently have the two tended to move together.

The Department of Labor has argued consistently that America's unemployment is structural in nature, and cannot be solved simply by increasing purchasing power. Its argument has gone like this:

Most of the new jobs now being created require High School education and the mentality of the white-collar worker. Thus, without an improvement in the quality of the available labour reserve, through education and re-training, an expansion in demand is liable to run into bottlenecks of qualified manpower without necessarily making much impact on total unemployment. The United States could find itself in the worst of all possible worlds – with inflation and unemployment combined.

The point is that, as industry becomes more complex and as the amount of capital required per worker increases, the threshold of employability goes up. It is estimated that, if boom conditions continue, the United States will be employing 65 per cent more professional and technical workers in 1975 than in 1960, but only 18 per cent more operatives and kindred workers. The unskilled jobs requiring a low standard of intelligence and education are disappearing with automation. The people who held, or in the past would have held, these jobs are not capable of doing the jobs which *are* available. They are in fact unemployable; it is simply not worth industry's while to install the large amounts of capital needed to provide them with jobs. This trend towards a higher minimum standard of ability as a condition of employment looks like going on; the threshold will probably continue to rise. And more and more people are likely to fall below it, on current trends, through lack of education. The nation's education is simply not matching up to the increasingly stringent needs of industry. And the danger is that a sub-class of unemployables will emerge and solidify, outside the country's productive machine, producing children whose educational standards will make them equally unemployable.

This is perhaps the biggest social danger facing the United States today – and the fact that a large proportion of this sub-class is Negro (and often deprived of educational facilities by the deliberate action of the local white majorities) merely intensifies the problem.

The Council of Economic Advisers to the President (C.E.A.) on the other hand, has argued that the Department of Labor overestimates the structural nature of America's unemployment and underestimates its cyclical aspect. The persistently high rate of unemployment, on this argument, is simply an index of inadequate demand. The United States should therefore aim to jack up its rate of increase in production to 6 per cent a year in real terms, until unemployment comes down to 4 per cent (as it did by early 1966). Thereafter the economy should aim to settle down to a steady growth-rate of 4 per cent a year in real terms, about half coming from increases in productivity and half from increases in the labour force. This would involve running industry at an average rate of 92 per cent of capacity – a rate which would enable overheads to be well covered but would not put an inflationary strain on resources. (The thinking here is interestingly aligned with that of the Paishians in London. The United States has been approaching the Paishian 'Golden Mean' from below, as it were – from a situation where there is an excessive reserve of manpower and equipment – whereas in Britain we have been regularly above it.)

The C.E.A. argued that the remarkable increases in productivity achieved by U.S. industry since 1960 are normal in the upswing period of the business cycle, and that they represented in part the delayed-action effect of the very heavy investment in new equipment and new techniques – including R. & D. –

during the years of comparative stagnation. If demand continued to expand, the effect of this massive injection of technology would start to wear off; productivity would stop rising quite so fast, and in order to expand output industry would have to start taking on new workers and so eating into the reserve army of the unemployed. In this case, industry's standards of employment would begin to drop and people previously regarded as unemployable would in fact be taken on; industry itself would have to assume more of the responsibility for training the workers it needed in the skills required.

As is so often the case, the evidence suggests that there is some truth on both sides. The massive tax cuts of 1964, and still more perhaps the pressure resulting from the Vietnam war, provided the economy with a new fillip of purchasing power in 1965, and by 1966 the 4 per cent unemployment target had been reached and the economy was at last showing signs of overheating and inflationary pressures. At the same time President Johnson, through the educational and 'anti-poverty' aspects of the Great Society programme, had begun an imaginative and courageous attack on the structural problems to which the Department of Labor had been drawing attention. More will however need to be done in this field, particularly in re-training and the improvement of educational facilities, if the United States is to maintain the recent rate of expansion over a period of years. And one of the many tragedies of the ghastly war in Vietnam is that it has deflected – one hopes only temporarily – American energies from the 'unfinished business' in the U.S. itself.

Early in 1966 the National Commission on Technology, Automation and Economic Progress appointed by Congress to study the problems of automation made the following recommendations among others:

(1) A guaranteed minimum income for every American family.

(2) A guarantee of high-school education for all Americans, or 14 years' free public education.

(3) A national computerized job–man matching system to provide better information on employment opportunities and available workers.

(4) Federal-administered employment agencies, with other measures to assist labour mobility.

(5) Regional economic development plans to be spearheaded by the Federal Reserve banks in each of their districts.

(6) A Federal Government drive to promote technology in the areas of transportation, housing, health and air and water pollution control. A Federal building code that would deny Federal aid to communities failing to adopt the code, aimed at preventing the construction of poorly built houses which degenerate into slums.

(7) Increased use of systems analysis to solve social and environmental problems.

(8) Greater use of public procurement and government aid to universities to promote technological advance, and measures to speed up the diffusion of knowledge from universities and government research institutions.

That a Commission appointed by Congress should recommend such radical measures is an indication of how markedly the climate of opinion in the United States has moved away from its traditional '*laissez faire*' posture towards Johnsonian 'consensus' in the last few years. It remains to be seen, however, how fruitful the Johnsonian approach will prove in tackling the problems posed by the unequal pace of technological advance, and the growing gap between the technologically advanced industries and the others. This is the so-called 'spill-over' problem, and – like the dispute between the 'structuralists' and the 'Keynesians' – it is directly relevant to us on this side of the Atlantic.

## Diffusing Technology

An uneven rate of technological advance and application is characteristic of all countries, both as between industries and between firms. It has been estimated that four fifths of the R. & D. scientists and engineers in U.S. industry are employed by the 350 largest corporations (which account for 60 per cent of gross national sales). Three industries – aerospace, electrical equipment and communications (including computers and electronics), and chemicals – account for 70 per cent of the total. Among the main low-research industries are textiles, machine tools, metal fabrication and building.[1]

There is, it is true, a partly self-correcting mechanism at work here, as the high-research industries increasingly invade the territory of the technologically backward. The invasion of the textile industries by the chemically-derived synthetics is one example of this process. Another is the introduction of new materials into building – such as plastics, pre-stressed concrete, aluminium – leading to the adoption of new techniques of pre-fabrication and flow-line production. Similarly, the development of numerically-controlled machine tools (largely as a result of research work done in the Air Force and M.I.T. into ways of machining complex aircraft parts[2]) has brought the aerospace and electronics companies into traditional machine-tool markets on a growing scale.

In some cases, therefore, the diffusion of advanced technology occurs through a natural process of industrial diversification. But this is by no means universal. And if diversification acts as an equilibrating factor, it is heavily offset by the disequilibrating factor of government involvement in R. & D., which falls very unevenly between different industries.

As we have seen, the investment of the Federal Government in research and technology is enormous. The rate of growth is now showing signs of levelling off but at a very high level. Three fifths of all the R. & D. work done in the United States – both in and outside industry – is government-financed (compared with only 16 per cent in 1936). The demand by government agencies for qualified scientists is straining the resources of the educational system and creating shortages in some cases in industry itself. And, inevitably, this public investment is heavily concentrated on areas of interest to government – essentially on defence and the space programme. Of the 340,000 scientists and engineers employed full-time on R. & D. in 1963 more than half were in two industries – aircraft and missiles accounting for 105,000, electrical equipment and communications for 75,000. Nine tenths of the R. & D. funds spent by the aerospace industry comes from the government, as against one fifth in the chemical industry. Once again, this concentration of research on certain key industries where the government is the main purchaser is not peculiar to the United States. It is, in varying degrees, a common pattern.

The U.S. Administration has been concerned to see that this huge scientific investment in defence and the space programme produces a reasonable 'fall-out' on civil technology – especially as the 'backlash' against the scientist which we have observed in U.S. industry has been having its repercussions in Congress, in connexion with the space programme. More and more voices have been raised in the last three years to question the way in which America is using her scientific resources, to ask whether the space programme should be allowed to divert scarce scientific manpower away from industry. In the government's two-pronged scientific drive, it is naturally the space programme rather than defence which has come under pressure, though it spends less and makes a more conscious effort to promote the maximum spill-over into civil technology. Until recently the government insisted, for example, that all patents arising out of work for the National Aeronautics and Space Administration (N.A.S.A.) should become Federal property and so available to all; this provision has, incidentally, made many companies reluctant to work for the N.A.S.A. as compared with the Defense Department, which makes no such stipulation.

Second, the government has established the most elaborate system for the retrieval of information from space research ever known. It has commissioned five independent research centres (not all of these are still active) to process and appraise for their possible civilian applications the innovations – averaging some 1,500 a year – coming out of the N.A.S.A.'s ten technical centres. Each technical centre has its own staff group responsible for seeing that these innovations are fed out, and the whole process of dissemination is supervised by a special Advisory Group appointed by the President. One of the Group's members summed up the objective to me thus:

Space is the big scientific input of the sixties, just as defence was in the forties; we have to organize its civilian exploitation in the same way that the defence discoveries of the forties – atomic energy, radar and so on – were exploited for civil technology in the fifties.

One can see what he meant. The potential civilian 'fall-out' from space research could be substantial: in energy, for example (fuel cells, thermo-electrical units, miniaturization of atomic power units); in communications (Telstar, telemetry, computerization); new materials (cryogenics, high temperature metallurgy), micro-miniaturization, medicine, and – last but not least – new management techniques like network analysis and systems engineering.

Substantial as this effort has been, the results have so far been disappointing. There is still very little evidence that the massive investment in space technology by the United States will produce an adequate commercial pay-off.

Nor is this an isolated problem. The U.S. Administration has been trying for some years to find ways of bridging the 'technology gap' between the advanced and the more backward industries – for example, building, textiles or the railways. It has been concerned to speed up the overall pace of technological growth by the more rapid and effective diffusion of existing knowledge – to try to do on the national scale what, as we have seen, the research consultants seek to do on the level of the individual firm.

In this objective it faces a number of built-in institutional problems. In the United States, compared, for example, with the United Kingdom or U.S.S.R., there are far fewer research institutes serving whole industries. The industry-wide research association, the typical base for industrial research in Britain, is, as we have seen, much less important in America. Moreover, America has hitherto lacked any equivalent of Britain's former Department of Scientific and Industrial Research (D.S.I.R.) or National Research Development Council (N.R.D.C.) – government organizations specifically charged with the promotion of research and development in private industry (see Chapter 5). Still more does it lack any equivalent of Britain's Ministry of Technology. Third, and most important of all, there is still – though under President Johnson a diminishing – lack of contact and mutual trust between the Federal Government and industry which does not exist to anything like the same extent in Britain or France (though it does to some extent in Italy and Western Germany), and which could be a serious drawback for the United States in the years ahead.

Many factors have contributed to this sense of alienation between industry and the Federal authorities. The anti-trust legislation which is a traditional cross for U.S. business is one; there is a fear that if one becomes too closely involved with Washington one may have to divulge information which could subsequently be used against one in the courts. (It is worth remembering that in the United States, the heartland of capitalism, leading businessmen have gone to gaol in recent years for fixing prices. This has not happened in Britain even under Socialist governments; nor does it seem remotely possible that it should.) Also, one must always remember that the United States is a vast country, and to large areas of it Washington is incredibly remote, both physically and mentally. The cosy intimacy which can be achieved in small, highly centralized countries like Britain and France is impossible in the vast spaces of the North American subcontinent. (This is of course a matter of degree. Compared, for example, with Eire or Sweden both Britain and France give the appearance of countries with remote and almost unapproachable bureaucracies.) In America, unlike Britain, government functions on three levels – local, State and Federal. In many sectors it is local or State legislation and regulations which determines the climate within which business operates.

Take for example the case of house-building, one of the major problem industries as regards technology. The problems of innovation in building will be discussed at greater length in a later chapter, but in the specifically U.S. context it is worth pointing out that there are 120,000 separate building firms in the country and that, while there are some giants in the industry, the average firm builds ten houses a year. Moreover, the industry operates under a profusion of building codes which vary from State to State and from town to town. How in these circumstances can one ensure the rapid spread and acceptance of new ideas and techniques? Possibly only by some such means as the mandatory Federal building code proposed by the Congressional Committee on Technology.

In the next forty years the United States is going to have to build about as many new dwellings as are in existence in the country today. The problem of lagging building technology can hardly, therefore, be brushed aside. At least equally important is the problem of transport. Here the need is for co-ordination, for thinking in terms of unified systems rather than of individual industries – of 'transport' rather than of 'railways' or 'airlines' – of function rather than of product. But it is difficult to achieve this sort of approach when one has eight separate Federal agencies involved, with little or no central co-ordination.

The U.S. Administration, like the British, has been groping towards an overall policy of modernization – with integrated policies in such areas as transport, urban renewal and regional planning, and in the application of the discoveries of science and technology to the benefit of the community as a whole. In some respects it has achieved remarkable success. A Department of Transportation has now been set up, under a Federal Cabinet Minister, with overall responsibility for transport coordination. Under Mr MacNamara, the Department of Defense has done a great deal to apply business techniques to the operations of government – in a way which Whitehall has only recently begun to copy – and thereby, not only to ensure that the U.S. taxpayer gets value for money, but also to spread the use of techniques like network analysis and the latest methods of cost accounting among the firms (and they are a wide section of U.S. industry) who work on defence contracts. (The Department has been, for example, one of the pioneers of systems building in the United States.)

One might also mention in this context the pioneering work of the M.I.T.R.E. (Massachusetts Institute of Technology Research Engineering) Corporation, established on a non-profit basis to provide objective technical advice for U.S. government agencies on systems planning and engineering for information and communications systems. Originally founded to provide technical support for the U.S. Air Force Semi-Automatic Ground Environment System (S.A.G.E.) – a computer-based system for detecting, identifying and tracking hostile aircraft – M.I.T.R.E. is now organized into six main groups dealing respectively with military problems, air traffic systems, systems planning, systems engineering, information systems and applied science laboratories: blending together the disciplines and the insights of civil and defence technology.

Another field where the U.S. Administration has been ahead of Whitehall is in the use of investment appraisal techniques to determine the validity of major capital projects in the public sector – particularly those involving the use of public money to back developments in private industry. These techniques, involving operational research, technical, cost/benefit and market studies carried out in government, universities and research organizations, enable the eventual political decisions

('Should we back this or not, and if so how far?') to be carried out on a basis of far more detailed information than has in the past been available to members of H.M. Government or their top civil servants when faced with similar decisions. Examples in recent years have been the 'Project Horizon' evaluation of the U.S. aircraft industry carried out in 1962, and the more recent studies on the supersonic transport plane to compete with the Anglo-French Concord. All this represents no more than the extension to the national level of the business techniques designed to facilitate rational management decision and reduce the area of uncertainty which we have been discussing in the last chapter. In the last few years these techniques have come increasingly to be used in Whitehall in such fields as defence and transport; but we still lag significantly behind the United States – as do most, if not all, of our European neighbours.

A further major step forward in technological policy in the United States was proposed in the State Technical Service Act approved by Congress in 1965. This Act sets out a programme of matching Federal–State grants for regional technological information centres, designed to help firms apply advanced technology to the extension of markets and to stimulate the creation of new technically based businesses. State plans would be formulated and put into effect with local initiative and responsibility. Each participating State is expected to submit a five-year technological development plan, certified by the State Governor, to the Office of the Assistant Secretary of Commerce for Science and Technology in Washington. Within this plan there is to be an annual technical services programme which identifies particular methods and contracts for achieving particular goals, with a detailed budget, and which also specifies the responsibilities assigned to each participating institution – educational or other – in the State.

Another powerful instrument for solving the diffusion problem in civil technology is the new Institute of Applied Technology set up as part of the Federal Bureau of Standards. The

Institute is concerned with improving the dissemination of new technical information to industry and business, to supplement the existing dissemination programmes such as those of N.A.S.A. and the Atomic Energy Corporation (A.E.C.). It has set up special groups on information processing, instrumentation, building, transportation and engineering standards, weights and measures. It will be responsible for the Federal operation of the State Technical Service Act. The Institute is also working on the development of criteria for industrial products, so as to lead to the development of performance-based codes and standards, thus aiding technological innovation; and on developing criteria of performance for Federal Government purchases, so that the formidable buying power of the central government can be used as a stimulus to innovation. Tax and other incentives to private concerns undertaking R. & D. projects have also been under study in Washington for some time.

All this indicates that the U.S. authorities are now making a systematic attempt (on the same broad lines as the Ministry of Technology in Britain – see Chapter 5) to achieve a more broadly based technological advance by a planned policy of diffusing technology. This is a major step forward, which in many ways runs against the grain of American conventional wisdom and institutional practice. Among the proliferation of Federal agencies and the ramifications of America's three-tier governmental structure it has hitherto proved virtually impossible to provide the sort of clear-cut coordinating machinery needed to remove the imbalances in American society. Moreover, the U.S. system of government, with its built-in conflicts between the executive and the legislature, between the Administration and Congress, with its carefully balanced separation of powers, has proved a major obstacle to swift and dynamic change.

In the Johnsonian heyday of 1965–6, the traditional tensions seemed to be easing. If this trend were to be maintained, it could have momentous consequences for the development of the U.S. economy and the future of the world. For the antagonisms lie very deep in the American psyche.

The idea, enshrined in the 'Neddy' concept, that government and industry (both sides of industry) should work together in partnership to develop the economy and spread the fruits of technology, is alien to the national consciousness. (President Kennedy, as we now know, had a warm personal admiration for French planning. But for reasons of domestic politics this penchant was kept a closely guarded secret from the American people.) In the American context trade unions are opponents of management: intelligent opponents who are prepared to treat with the other side, and resolve their differences peacefully where possible – but still, in the last analysis, opponents owing no common loyalty. In the American context, too, the prevailing relationship between business enterprises is one of ruthless competition (and if they fail to fulfil this relationship, the resources of the Federal Government may be brought to bear on them). And, in the American context, government is expected to 'keep its nose out of business' (so long as business is competing, so long as it is not too heavily embarrassed by foreign imports, so long as there is an adequate flow of public works and other government contracts).

This does not mean that Americans are averse to planning as such. On the contrary, as we have seen, American corporate planning is of a scale and sophistication as to dwarf whatever is being done on the corporation level anywhere else in the world – not excluding the state-owned enterprises of the Soviet Union. This is because the management tools available in the United States are much better than those yet available in other countries. The difficulty has hitherto come when one tries to translate what is done within the corporation to national level. The basic trouble is that Americans do not trust their government – not because it is Democratic or Republican, but simply because it is government, and therefore alien to the national creed of rugged individualism – at best a necessary evil, at worst a sinister menace to the liberty of the individual.

It is easy for a European to argue that Americans who talk in this way are living in the past, that the days of the Open Frontier, when every man with guts and initiative could carve out a living for himself without any help from the state, ceased to apply three decades and more ago. But all nations have their national myths, and in America – precisely because it is a country of immigrants, where people have had to be taught how to be Americans in a way which does not apply in the older, homogeneous European societies – these myths are particularly pervasive. In the mythic drama of America the Federal Government has hardly even a walk-on role. (If anything, it is the character who gets the cheap laughs by slipping on the banana skin.) Of course the involvement of the public authorities in American enterprise has always been a good deal greater and a good deal more constructive than is generally understood. But powerful vested interests have operated to reinforce the national prejudice against 'big government', and – as has been wisely said – Americans tend to judge private industry by its successes but government by its failures.

How much has this been altered by the events and achievements of the last few years? It is probably too early to say – though the signs (despite Vietnam) are encouraging. The Republican platform in the 1964 election represented a simon-pure appeal to the archetypal American myth to the point of caricature. Its staggering defeat opened the way for a reassessment of American realities, for the elaboration of a consensus between the role of the public and private sector in modern society.

It is of enormous importance to America and the world that the Johnsonian consensus should be lasting and fruitful. For unless the power of America's traditional myths can be lastingly weakened, and the conditions created in which a genuine partnership in progress can be forged between government and industry, there is a danger that much of her marvellous inventiveness will continue to run to waste, and that the imbalances and distortions in American society – the Galbraithian distortion of 'private affluence and public squalor', the 'poverty in the midst of plenty' caused by technological unemployment, the 'technological gap' between advanced and backward industries, the misuse of resources through lack of any coordinating plan – will intensify. America's basic need was best expressed by E. M. Forster in another context ... 'Only connect'. I am reminded of the words of one of Washington's leading technologists, in private conversation in 1963:

We're going to have to coordinate our activities the way the Russians seem to. That means getting our priorities right. It's much more important to be ahead in operations research than to be first on the Moon. And it also means getting a better-integrated kind of society.

NOTES TO CHAPTER THREE

1. The distinction between 'technologically advanced' or 'science-based' industries and others is of course one of degree rather than of kind. It can be argued that *all* industries today are, or ought to be, 'science-based'; and it is certainly true that in all industries there are some concerns which are much more technologically advanced than others. Nevertheless, the average degree of technological penetration does vary substantially from industry to industry as from firm to firm.

2. See *Industry in the U.S.A.*, by Geoffrey Owen (Penguin Books, 1965), p. 159.

# CHAPTER FOUR

# THE UNITED STATES – LESSONS FOR EUROPE

WHAT lessons emerge from America's experience of the technological revolution of the last few years? First, the problem is not
the pace of discovery but the pace of its application, the speed
with which new ideas, techniques and inventions can be diffused
through industry and society and absorbed. This is partly a
question of improving our techniques for the dissemination of
information. It is significant that the last few years have seen
the emergence of a completely new specialist expertise in the
shape of the Information Scientist – whose function is not to
discover new things but, equally valuable, to find out what has
been discovered elsewhere which could be relevant to his own
company or organization, and to see that research work being
done in his company is not duplicated by work done elsewhere.
The problem of organizing the production of research to
minimize waste of effort is becoming increasingly serious as its
volume increases.

But this is only part of the problem. The other, and more
complex, part is to ensure that management is able to exploit and
utilize the work of the technologists and scientists. This is
partly a question of company structure – rigidly formalized
chains of command do not encourage the free flow of ideas
which is required – and partly a question of the motivation
and skill of management itself. We have seen that the efforts
of the R. & D. department can often be wasted through lack
of contact with management, and that this is more likely to
occur when management is defensive-minded (and therefore
psychologically averse to innovation) and/or technologically
unskilled.

## Managers and Mobility

One of the necessary antidotes to the sclerosis of management is greater mobility. America has benefited from the fact that she has always been a remarkably mobile society. Business executives have always tended to move much more freely from company to company than has been normal in Europe – and in consequence ideas and techniques have tended to move more rapidly also. And not only between firms; a MacNamara can apply in the Department of Defense the lessons learned from running Ford Motors. Mobility has been stimulated further in recent years by the growth of professional management selection, and of the executive search industry – the so-called 'body snatchers' who act as undercover recruitment agents for expanding organizations. (In some cases these concerns place spies in large companies to try to find out which promising executives there are dissatisfied or frustrated and might therefore respond to an offer from another potential employer. Naturally they are disliked by many U.S. businesses, but on balance they seem to fulfil a most useful function.)

Two other forces promoting mobility, of men and of ideas, are the consultants (including the contract research firms like Arthur D. Little) and the growth of management education in U.S. universities. The importance of management education is that it provides managers with a common framework of knowledge and ideas and a common 'language'. In this way it facilitates movement, because it enables a man to apply what he has been taught in a new and unexpected situation. A man whose whole experience of management has been in, say, machine tools might feel somewhat out of his depth if asked to run a retail drapery business. But if he has had some education in business management he will at least have some basis to work from. He may still make some ghastly mistakes, but equally he may introduce some good new ideas.

The role of the consultants and the contract research firms in spreading techniques and technology, in cross-fertilizing and catalysing, is equally apparent. I have stressed the role of the contract research firm, partly because of the contrast to the way in which research is typically organized in Britain through the research association. The research association, occupying a half-way house between the pure research of the university laboratory and the R.&D. department of the individual firm which must be ruled by the tyranny of the profit-and-loss account, is in many ways a typically British answer to a complex problem. It carries a semi-official aura, it is not directly involved in the sordid question of commercial viability. It is a good instrument for diffusing technology throughout a given industry. But it is likely to be less effective in applying research techniques to particular corporate problems demanding a hard commercial answer. Ideally there should be a place for both types of research organization in a modern economy. Much of the relative strengths and weaknesses of the British and American responses to the challenge of innovation reflects the contrast between the two types of organization.

The second, and more fundamental, reason why I think the contract research firm has lessons for us in Europe is that it represents, in microcosm, the sort of crossing of disciplines which is increasingly involved in tackling the problems of technological advance. The diffusion of technology requires, above all else, the breaking down of man-made barriers – barriers between specialisms, barriers between pure and applied research, between industry and university, between different departments in the big corporation, and so on. (We shall develop this theme further in subsequent chapters.)

Because the United States is a more mobile, more fluid, less stratified society than ours, it has less difficulty in applying these lessons. America also has the advantage of being culturally much more business-oriented than we are in Britain. The general level of awareness of business is far higher. The intellectual who is proud of the fact that he does not know the first thing about business organization, still a depressingly common figure in English life, is almost non-existent in the United States. Business matters are discussed far more freely in the U.S. press than in Britain or the Continent. And – part cause, part effect – the tradition of business reticence about its affairs which is still so strong in Europe is far less in evidence in America. All this helps to promote a swifter flow of ideas and to accelerate the flow of innovation.

Nevertheless, management still has lessons to learn in the United States about the utilization of technology. The question of appraising the value of R. & D. still troubles many firms. Can innovation be reconciled with planning? Can research be programmed? How can one calculate a reasonable return on R. & D. investment? No one would claim that the answers to these questions have been definitively demonstrated as yet. Indeed, in a swiftly changing environment management's search for certainty in an uncertain world becomes almost daily more agonizing.

## The Systems Approach

The other great lesson which management still has to learn in many cases is the need to think, not in terms of product, but in terms of function: not in terms of telephones, for example, but of communications – not railways but transportation. Too many business managers, in the United States as elsewhere, accept as immutable data their existing range of products, methods and activities. They do not start by asking themselves the basic question: 'Why am I doing this? What am I trying to achieve?'

But if one *does* start asking oneself these basic questions, one is quickly led into asking: 'What other ways are there of achieving the same ultimate purpose?' – and: 'Are all of these other ways more expensive, or slower, or more wasteful of resources?' And one starts to ask oneself: 'What long-term expenses does our project involve and would one of the different routes to the same ultimate aim be less expensive in the long run?'

This is what is meant by the term 'systems approach' or 'systems engineering' which has been so widely used in the United States in the last few years. The arch-priests of the systems approach are the organizers of the Bell Telephone system, whose commercial laboratories are regarded by many objective observers as perhaps the best in the world, and whose handling of the American telecommunications network is one of the undoubted wonders of modern capitalism. The Bell organization has always seen its role as being the improvement of communications as such, and it has coordinated the work of all its employees – scientists, engineers, salesmen – to this task. It was the Bell laboratories that discovered the transistor in 1948. This invention arose from basic research into solid-state physics begun during the thirties. Having applied its discovery to the improvement of telecommunications, the parent company A.T. & T. (American Telephone and Telegraph Company) with a mixture of logic and public spirit decided to make available to other companies the results of its research, and so enabled the semi-conductor industry to come into being.

The four basic principles of systems engineering have been described as follows:

(1) To appraise need and feasibility;

(2) To evaluate alternatives for achieving the desired result;

(3) To distinguish between what is known and not known;

(4) To identify opportunities for the creation and evolution of systems that meet functional needs and to identify related obstacles and means for their removal.

(Following the same principles, A.T. & T. has recently been conducting research into, *inter alia*, possible commercial applications of telepathy – a form of communication which could conceivably have interesting implications for the company's basic hardware!)

In contrast to America's success in the communications field has been the failure so far to evolve an integrated transport system – partly because of the product-orientated thinking, until recently, of railway management, partly because of the proliferation of regulating authorities in the public sector, partly because of the lack of the systems approach. The problem of railway rationalization has been baffling Americans for nearly half a century. A major programme of government-backed research into various aspects of the public transport problem is now under way: notably into the feasibility of a system of high-speed rail services linking Boston, New York and Washington – the so-called Northeast Corridor. Some of the work being done in connexion with this project, at M.I.T. in particular, on revolutionary new forms of commuter rail transport, is visionary in concept and is potentially of great importance. But the project as a whole falls a long way short of the full-scale investigation into an integrated public transport system linked to industrial and planning objectives for which the protagonists of systems engineering have been arguing.

These are the problems for management today. For the future, other complications present themselves. How is today's executive, working full-time at his job, to keep abreast of the expansion of knowledge in his field? It is not enough to say that he can keep his business up to date by using consultants. The consultancy business is beginning, particularly in the U.S., to become overcrowded; and as more and more people come into it, the proportion of charlatans is probably on the increase. There is, unfortunately, no sure-fire way of distinguishing a good consultant from a bad one. The increasing complexity of the terminology employed – almost every consultant today peddles his own range of techniques, often differing only verbally from those of his competitors - makes it more difficult for the inexpert manager to find his way through the maze. The only solution is for the manager himself to remain *au courant* with the development of the relevant technology and with the latest business techniques.

This is likely to have increasingly important implications for company structure. One possibility is a much more rapid throughput of managers, with quicker promotion and much earlier retirement and/or demotion to less onerous work at a fairly early age. (One British electronics company today reckons the useful life of its top executives at about five years – and this in a country which tends to put a much higher premium on stability than the United States.)

Alternatively, it may be necessary to establish a convention that business executives, like university professors, need a regular sabbatical year to re-charge their batteries and catch up with technical developments. In this case management structures need to be made more flexible than they commonly are today – so that executives can leave their desks for longish periods without disrupting the work of the organization, and resume them without disappointing ambitions and causing internal friction. These problems can of course be solved, but industry in America and elsewhere is going to need to give more thought to them in the future than it has hitherto.

The impact of computer technology on management structures and methods has in any case yet to be fully absorbed. It is becoming more widely recognized in U.S. business that the real function of a computer is not just to perform automatically processes which had previously been done in some other way. Its real function is to provide 'insight' rather than 'numbers' – to 'provide an integrated centralized data processing service for the control of the total company operation'.[1] This involves the reorganization of company information systems, decision-making procedures and therefore the management structure. It means, in effect, that management becomes much less concerned with organizing, processing and analysing information – and this has traditionally been a large part of the job of middle management – and much more concerned with using this information to take decisions.

This has a number of implications for structure. It increases the importance and numbers of top management at the expense of middle management, so that the hierarchy becomes flattened and, in traditional terms, top-heavy rather than pyramidal. The simplification of relations between senior and middle managers means that the former's 'span of control' is broadened – he can control more than the traditional number of immediate subordinates. This in turn complicates problems of management succession, since the ranks of middle management from which the successors to today's top management would normally be drawn are depleted by the impact of the new technology.

Instead, we tend to see the emergence of two separate power structures in the organization: senior management on the one hand, and the computer specialists who command the new skills on the other. Sometimes senior management may have the expertise of the second group, but by no means always. Some commentators on the current U.S. business scene suspect the growing power of the new class of technical experts, arguing that as a group they have no loyalty to the organization, no real commercial sense, no sense of human needs and values, but that they are prepared to subordinate everything to the search for a totally rational and self-consistent business system. We see here echoes of the arguments which have occupied us in earlier chapters. It is not necessary to take sides in this dispute. What is clear is that business in the United States, as elsewhere, has to adapt itself to the demands of the new technology. It has to learn to live with its 'new men', and, in the process of learning from them, to teach them also. It is hardly surprising that some sectors of U.S. enterprise find this process harder than others.

So far as business itself is concerned, however, the United States is better equipped to meet the challenge of technology than any other major industrial country. The moral that we have been stressing so far in this book is that the more open and liberal a society, the less compartmentalized by rigid barriers, the easier it will be to exploit the discoveries of science; and also the more open to new ideas and disciplines is the educational system, the less subject to the demarcation of academic frontier-lines drawn up in a pre-scientific age, the more rapidly can innovation proceed. In both these respects American society has, it seems to me, a clear advantage over the societies of Europe – on both sides of the Iron Curtain.

## The Role of the State

But this, as we have seen, is not the whole problem. There is another party involved – the state. As financier of research, as buyer of technology, as climate-setter for business, the role of the state in promoting innovation is inescapable. We have seen how, in Britain, national planning has developed as a logical extension of the market research function carried on within the individual firm. This logic, one would think, applies equally to business in the United States. It is true that government economic policy has not fluctuated anything like so sharply, or so disastrously for industry, in America as in Britain. But the fluctuations of the consumer market have been substantially greater; and, while 'Neddy-type' planning cannot of course eliminate this factor, it ought to be of some help in predicting major shifts in the market. (It is no answer to cite, as opponents of planning naturally do, some of the worst failures of market forecasting in the past; the answer to bad planning is not no planning, but good planning. No business man is likely to decide to dispense with sales forecasting altogether because one sales forecast goes wrong. He is more likely to sack the staff and get himself a better team.)

But the United States has not hitherto been ready or equipped, as we have seen, to create a durable partnership between business and government, or to integrate the processes of decision-making at national level. America is a highly integrated society – up to the point where government starts to intrude. Thereafter it has traditionally been a remarkably disintegrated society, in which decision-making tends to be uncoordinated and the diffusion of technology slow and uncertain (despite, as stated above, the remarkable achievements of men like Mr MacNamara at the Defense Department). In this respect America is at a disadvantage compared with the Soviet Union or France – or even, in certain respects, the United Kingdom. Each of these countries has the power and the machinery to focus national efforts on particular priorities in a way which the United States cannot, except in exceptional circumstances, do.

Thus despite the progress made in the last few years, the United States authorities still lack some crucial weapons. The government lacks the necessary powers – such as the standby tax-changing authority sought by President Kennedy in 1961 – to ward off impending recession or inflation. Though much has been done in the last few years, the government's manpower and re-training policies have been hampered by the reluctance of Congress to provide adequate funds; this has almost certainly kept unemployment higher than it would otherwise have been. In the field of technology, the application of government-sponsored research to civilian industries like building and machine tools has been resisted on the grounds of governmental usurpation of the functions of private enterprise.

This is not to say that the sort of centralization found in Russia or France (in very different circumstances, of course) is in every way preferable to the type of set-up in the United States. We have here another manifestation of the perennial conflict referred to earlier between Order and Creativity. In the Soviet Union and France the emphasis is on Order (in the Russian case because of ideology and political structure, in the French case because of the Cartesian tradition in thought and education); in America the emphasis lies heavily on Creativity. If one has to choose between these two absolutes, one must, I think, choose Creativity. Certainly the record so far supports the United States against all comers. In space technology, it is true, the Soviet Union can show remarkable achievements – but largely because of a concentration of effort which it would probably be hard to justify on rational grounds. One does not have to spend long in Russia to note the extreme disparity in technical advance and efficiency between the different sectors of national life. And, to a much greater extent even than in America, the technologically advanced areas are those in which the state is particularly interested. If the concentration of resources in the hands of the central authorities stifles the creative atmosphere in which science and innovation flourish – or if, by virtue of false priorities, they distort its development – then one must say the price is too high to pay.

But is this stark choice necessary? Is it not possible to reconcile the demands of Order and Creativity? The fear of the Federal Government, as we have seen, is largely an illusory fear based on a national myth which has lost all touch with present-day American reality – the myth of the frontier perpetuated in suburbia (rather as the Establishment-cosseted Labour Party leaders in Britain still sing, at the close of Party conferences, the supremely irrelevant lyrics of the 'Red Flag'). I have talked above of the huge concentration of effort in Soviet technology. But this may be changing. The most impressive feature of Russia today is the enormous output of highly trained graduate technologists, scientists and engineers. As this generation moves into Soviet industry, we are going to see an increasingly rapid broadening-out of the scope of technological advance; particularly if, as seems likely, the state adopts a more intelligent strategy for innovation, one less geared to prestige projects. One has to remember that in Russia there are no institutional barriers to the dissemination of technology – no patent laws, no overt conflicts between state and business, no 'brain drain' of scientists.

This is the danger facing the United States – that its present technological lead could disappear in the face of a more purposefully oriented society. And it is so unnecessary. Already the resources of the state are heavily geared to promoting innovation in two strictly limited areas – defence and space. Why, ask the new thinkers in Washington, cannot the same resources be used on a broader scale to keep America ahead in the race that really matters – the race to exploit the discoveries of technology for the maximization of the nation's wealth and happiness, and for the betterment of mankind? The challenge facing America is not a technical one, it is a challenge of social, political and psychological adjustment, to adapt the ideals of the eighteenth century to the facts of the twentieth. As the wagon trains of the Great Society head off for the moonlit prairie, they carry with them the hopes and the envy of pioneering spirits in other and less favoured lands.

NOTE TO CHAPTER FOUR

1. See 'How the Computer Changes Management', by Enid Mumford and Tom Ward, *New Society*, 23 September 1965.

# CHAPTER FIVE

# GOVERNMENT AS INNOVATOR

IN the last three chapters I have tried, inevitably somewhat impressionistically, to list some aspects of recent American experience that might be relevant to Britain and to Europe. In the next three chapters I propose to look at the implications of these in terms of, consecutively, government, management and the trade unions. I propose to look at what is happening already in this country, at what is likely to happen, and at what needs to happen if Britain is to take full advantage of the opportunities modern technology offers.

In October 1964, for the first time in thirteen years, Britain returned a Labour government to power. As in 1945, the policies fashioned in opposition had been largely designed to cope with conditions of industrial stagnation, while in fact – as in 1945 – the immediate domestic economic problem was rather one of inflationary pressure on resources; and, as in 1945, there was an initial slowness to recognize the strength of these inflationary pressures. At the same time, the Wilson government inherited an appalling balance-of-payments crisis. The deficit on current and capital payments – an unparalleled £769 million for the year as a whole – quickly developed, partly as a result of somewhat unskilled handling by the incoming administration, into a serious run on the pound. The government, determined to avoid devaluation, found itself forced to take measures to improve the balance of payments which ran counter to its long-term plans for industrial investment and social reform. Some £900 million of foreign debt was incurred. And, like his predecessors, the Labour Chancellor found himself increasingly forced into deflationary policies in order to protect the pound and reduce the payments deficit.

For a time, however, things went reasonably well. The high point of the Wilson administration's fortunes came with the March 1966 election, at which the government's overall majority went up from 3 to 97. At that time the government was able to claim that it had gone more than half way towards eliminating the balance-of-payments deficit without having had to resort to any net increase in unemployment or any actual reduction in production. Investment in industry had been maintained, and the underemployed development regions in the North and West had been successfully shielded from the deflationary measures applied to the overheated Midlands and South-East. Mr Wilson and his colleagues were able to claim that their management of the economy was of a higher order than that of their predecessors, in that they had been able to reverse an unfavourable balance of payments without resort to 'stop–go'. The 1970 National Plan, published in 1965, which forecast a 25-per-cent increase in gross national product between 1964 and 1970, explicitly assumed that it would be possible to combine a favourable balance of payments with uninterrupted full employment and improved productivity.

There was, however, another side to the picture. The reduction in the balance-of-payments deficit was achieved with the aid of a temporary surcharge on imports and restraints on overseas investments which, however necessary, could have adverse long-term effects on British exports. Moreover, the continued tightness of the labour market (which surprised the government almost as much as it did outside observers) meant that the pressure on wages and prices continued to be excessive, despite the valiant efforts of the authorities to contain it. And, while output *did* continue to rise in 1965 and early 1966, in spite of government restraints, the rise was disappointingly small – given that the effective limit on output was set, not by the market (the rise in wages and the high level of employment meant that there was no lack of demand for goods in Britain in 1965 and early 1966) but by industry's inability to increase productivity fast enough. Throughout this period, in fact, the economy was bumping uncomfortably against the ceiling set by the availability of resources – particularly of labour: availability, that is, *given the current degree of efficiency in their utilization*. In the event, Britain's productivity grew during this period at an annual rate of around $2\frac{1}{2}$ per cent – depressingly low by international standards.

During the summer of 1966 the situation rapidly worsened. The balance-of-payments recovery petered out, and inflationary pressures developed again, fed by wage and price increases. A run on sterling began of even greater virulence than that of 1964. In July 1966 the government was compelled to bring in deflationary measures which brought the boom to an abrupt end, caused the index of production to fall sharply and unemployment to rise, and completely invalidated the forecasts of the National Plan. In spite of themselves, Mr Wilson and his colleagues had become Paishians. 'Stop–go', said the cynics, had been replaced by 'stop'.

In the early part of 1967 these measures appeared to be having the desired effect – at least in the short term. The rise in costs of British industry was slowed down appreciably, exports rose and imports fell. But the obverse of this was, of course, a decline in growth of productivity – and, more worrying from the long-term point of view, a sharp downturn in industrial investment. Was Britain once again mortgaging the future for the present, jeopardizing long-term competitiveness for the sake of short-term solvency?

The first two years of Mr Wilson's government showed, in fact, that there was no *short-term* solution to the problems of the British economy – given the overall framework set by the role and exchange rate of sterling and our world-wide trading relationships. The problem remains as described in Chapter 1. Unless we can improve the way in which we use our resources – by greater productivity, greater efficiency, a faster application of technology, more effective management – we shall not be able to secure reasonably fast rates of economic growth for more than short periods without running into inflation and payments difficulties. Unless we can improve the *long-term* structure of our economy we cannot solve our persistent *short-term* problems. This will be true under any form of government we may choose.

In fact the Labour government has done a considerable amount to lay the foundation for long-term reforms in the structure and functioning of the economy, particularly through co-operation between industry and government. Its mistake may have been to expect these to produce results too quickly, particularly in a climate which because of overheating was not necessarily conducive to improved competitiveness. (It is too early to say whether the cold climate which succeeded in the second half of 1966 will prove more or less beneficial.) It has not made its task easier by some of its own actions. I propose to spend the rest of this chapter discussing these longer-term measures, particularly those associated with the two major new departments of State – the Department of Economic Affairs and the Ministry of Technology. Since I have been directly involved in a number of these measures,[1] the reader may find the tone of this chapter somewhat more *engagé* and less dispassionate than other sections of this book. I make no attempt in this chapter to draw up a definitive balance sheet of advantage and disadvantage from these somewhat radical changes. It is still much too early to attempt such a task. I would merely record my (possibly prejudiced) view that the experiment on which I and many others have been engaged has been consistently exciting, no doubt misguided in places, but on the whole more likely to succeed than any visible alternative.

## The Road to Intervention

Within the first days of Labour's victory in October 1964, two key new ministries were created in the economic–industrial field – the Department of Economic Affairs under the deputy premier Mr George Brown (subsequently Mr Michael Stewart), and the Ministry of Technology under Mr Frank Cousins (subsequently Mr Anthony Wedgwood Benn).

These two departments were to carry a long stage further the trend towards increasing governmental intervention in industry which had already, as we have seen, begun at the end of the fifties. Other factors, besides the revival of the concept of planning, underlay this sea-change. Many were quite non-ideological in character. One factor, for example, has been the need to ensure a satisfactory return from the huge investments of the nationalized industries; another the escalating technological complexity of the hardware required by the armed services. For a variety of reasons the state now finds itself responsible for more than 40 per cent of all national expenditure – and increasingly involved, also, in guiding the activities of the private sector which accounts for the remaining 55–60 per cent. Moreover, those purchases for which the state is directly responsible include some of the most technologically advanced and complex equipment of all. The necessary involvement of the state appears to increase as technology advances. This, as we have seen, has been true of the United States. It has been, and will be increasingly, true not only of the United Kingdom but of all technologically advanced countries.

In order to meet these new responsibilities, government has had to acquire new skills and in some cases to re-think old attitudes.[2] The philosophy of much of Whitehall has traditionally been essentially *laisser faire* in orientation. Few leading administrative civil servants have had direct experience of work in industry – though there are some significant exceptions. Some departments in the past have been less ready than others to recruit specialists, or to give sufficient responsibility in policy-making to those they did employ. (It is fair to say that the same criticism could be advanced of much of British industry and almost all British trade unions.)

Some commentators in recent years have compared the British civil service elite with the technologically trained *polytechnicien* in France, and have pointed out that the latter, who has increasingly come to occupy leading posts in government, in industry and the planning network, has an apparently much greater occupational mobility between the three. This freer movement, they have argued, not only makes for a more efficiently operated mixed economy, but also helps to promote the rapid diffusion of ideas and techniques which, as we have seen, is one of the main requirements for successful innovation.

This comparison is, I believe, an oversimplification. Nevertheless, it contains an element of truth. It oversimplifies by ignoring the respective roles of the civil servants' political masters in the two countries. Ministers, after all, are the ultimate decision-makers in Whitehall. Also, it blends together an argument on *education* and an argument on *administration*. It is, I think, undeniable that the British educational tradition is essentially humanist, and that our technological development has suffered from the traditional undervaluation (in contrast with, for example, Germany) of technology in our educational system and philosophy. This is now changing, and changing fairly rapidly. It is also true that the senior echelons of the civil service, like the senior echelons of other sections of our national life, tend to reflect the educational system which produced them. But this too is changing.

The *administrative* argument is that there has been insufficient cross-fertilization of ideas and experience between government, industry, trade unions and the educational system, that there has been excessive compartmentalization between the different sectors of our national life. This argument does not necessarily follow from the first, though the two often tend to be confused in public discussion. But it is now almost universally accepted that if the experiment in planning is to continue, if we are to continue to operate a mixed economy with a substantial degree of governmental involvement in industry, if we are to accelerate the successful application of technology, we need a greater degree of mobility of ideas and people between Whitehall and the other main interests involved.

This is now happening. The government now tries, through its Centre for Administrative Studies, to provide its young civil servants with a greater understanding of some of the specialist skills required in administration. The recruitment of outside experts into government, usually on short-term secondment, has been radically increased since October 1964 – notably, but by no means exclusively, into the new departments of State. I believe this trend is now irreversible whatever party is in power. Talks have started with the C.B.I. on ways of institutionalizing the mutual secondment of people between industry and government. The advice and guidance of leading businessmen is being increasingly sought to solve problems in the public sector. Government is moving increasingly into the market-place out of the somewhat monastic seclusion in which its mysteries have traditionally been practised.

This seems to me an immensely important and valuable development. Possibly it could go faster. The forthcoming report of the Fulton Committee on the Civil Service may have some further suggestions to make in this direction. But one should not underrate what has already been done.

## D.E.A., Neddy and the Treasury

Towards the end of 1963 I was invited to join a small group of Fabians who had been asked by the then Leader of the Opposition to consider whether there was a case for a new government department to complement the work of the Treasury in economic policy, and if so to draw up a blueprint for the work and organization of such a department. Our investigations led us to the conclusion that there was indeed a strong case for such a department – not to derogate from the work of existing ministries, but to cope with the increasing range of governmental responsibilitics cnvisaged in the Labour Party's policy, and to permit a more positive, interventionist approach to industry and the economy. This was the origin of the Department of Economic Affairs, or D.E.A.

Our arguments of establishing a second economics ministry (leaving aside questions of personalities, which are always important in politics but which hardly came within our remit) were as follows. First, we felt that the Treasury had acquired, by default, over the years a range of responsibilities which went beyond, and in some ways conflicted with, its traditional responsibilities for the balance of payments, for fiscal and monetary policy, for the stability of sterling, for ensuring that neither the government nor the nation as a whole overspent. These responsibilities, which were plainly of over-riding importance, did not necessarily square with re-sponsibility for economic growth and industrial efficiency, which seemed to have landed on the Treasury's lap almost by accident.

We felt that in any argument over policy the Treasury would be bound, by virtue of its traditions and its internal power structure, to give overriding weight to the claims of stability wherever these appeared to conflict with those of growth. Nor did we feel that the existence of Neddy, or the reconstruction carried out inside the Treasury in 1962, were enough to ensure that the argument for growth had adequate weight in Whitehall. Second, we felt that the Treasury lacked the knowledge to assume a direct responsibility for growth, which must inevitably depend on improving industrial efficiency. We felt that the Treasury, whose links with the outside world have always been mainly through other government departments, was not sufficiently in touch with industry to play the interventionist role which would be needed to promote purposeful growth; nor did we feel that it had adequate access to industry to act as an effective planning department. To put the argument another way, the Treasury's approach has always been a 'macro' one,

designed to achieve a balance at the national level between demand and supply. This is an indispensable function. But growth
depends on improving the supply side of the economy, through
a series of activities at the 'micro' level of the individual industry
or enterprise. An economy can balance its books, as Keynes
taught, at a high level of activity or at a low one. It was the job of
the Treasury, as we saw it, to see that the books balanced. It
should be the job of the new department, we felt, to see that the
balance was achieved at a high level rather than a low one – by
acting in the first instance on the supply side of the equation.

Was the alternative, then, to build up the leading production
department, the Board of Trade, into a kind of super-ministry
of industry, with equal status to the Treasury? After a good deal
of heart-searching we decided against this, for reasons which I
still believe in retrospect were cogent. The Board of Trade had
an unfortunate history in the late fifties and early sixties. As part
of the Conservative government's doctrine of disengagement
from industry, its industrial section was depleted and allowed to
run down. When the tide of policy turned at the end of the
decade, the Board – believing firmly in *laisser faire*, distrustful
of Neddy and the other innovations, fearful of becoming a target
for protectionist lobbies in industry – remained out of the swim.
It was not until 1965 that the approach became more flexible.
Until then the Board's unwillingness to assume a more positive,
interventionist role towards industry left an administrative
vacuum to be filled.

We felt that it would not be feasible to graft new functions on
to the Board of Trade, partly because of its general ideology,
but more particularly because of the enormous range of day-to-
day administrative work which falls within the Board's responsibilities. We feared that these administrative functions would
tend to smother any new, higher-level activities injected into the
department. Moreover, the Board of Trade had sponsorship
responsibilities for a number of industries, but by no means for
all. This could create an anomalous position *vis-à-vis* other

production ministries. We felt in principle that a department which was charged with general responsibility for the whole economy ought not to have particular overriding responsibility for any section of it. (As we shall see, this logic was not followed in the creation of the Ministry of Technology.)

The alternative to grafting new functions on to an existing department like the Board of Trade was to create an entirely new one, which would have to work through other departments to a considerable extent: a department analogous to the Treasury, if lacking the influence over other departments which accrues to the Treasury through its power of the purse.

The job of the D.E.A., then, is to *get growth* – which means, in the British context, to get more efficiency: not by compulsion, but by coordination, initiation and stimulation. The 1970 National Plan, published in September 1965 in replacement of the Neddy Plan described in Chapter 1, provided the department with (in effect) its charter.[3] The Plan remains a seminal document for policy making despite its defects, and despite the fact that its forecasts have been virtually disowned by the government in the light of the July 1966 crisis measures. For the 1970 Plan is the first to have been prepared in and by government, and its publication therefore represented for the first time an overt government commitment to a definite rate of economic growth. It is a tragedy (and a comment on the weaknesses of the Plan) that this particular commitment should so quickly have been proved worthless. But there is little doubt that the fashion of national planning has come to stay, and government policies will increasingly be built around and related to future National Plans. This is a development of fundamental long-term importance.

It means, for example, that the decisions of individual government departments must – for the first time – be directly related to an overriding national plan. It should no longer be possible for government departments to make claims for money and plans for expenditure on an entirely *ad hoc* basis, or for different

departments to pursue different and frequently unrelated policies. Not the least of the Plan's merits is that it is a means of
imposing discipline and coherence on the spending plans of
Whitehall.

Moreover, the Plan provides a framework for government
economic and industrial policy as a whole. It is not just, like the
Neddy Green Book, an exercise in model-building. It includes
also the more important Neddy Orange Book function of setting
out the policies and conditions needed to make the Plan a reality
as opposed to an aspiration.

What are these conditions? First, the government must create
the right *climate for growth* – a climate which mixes competitive
pressures and underlying expansion in the right proportions,
which rewards innovation and dynamism and penalizes sloth
and inefficiency: easy to state, considerably less easy to achieve.

Second, the government must seek to ensure that the nation's
limited resources are steered into those parts of the economy
where they will be most productive, and that the nation's
infrastructure – schools, houses, communications, etc. – is
adequate to sustain the rate of industrial growth needed, without
pre-empting too large a share of national investment capital.

Third, it is clearly essential – as we saw in Chapter 1 – that
prices remain competitive with those of other nations, and that
incomes do not outstrip production. Prices and incomes policy
is, as we have seen, an inseparable concomitant of planning for
growth, and it has been a major aspect of the D.E.A.'s work.
Mr George Brown succeeded where Mr Maudling had failed,
in persuading both sides of industry to agree to a policy for
keeping prices and incomes in line with productivity. But in the
inflationary conditions of 1965 and early 1966, translation of
principles into action proved extremely difficult. Wages continued to rise rapidly, prices less rapidly but still a good deal
faster than production.

To investigate and advise on particular cases where price or
income movements appear out of line with national norms, the

government set up in 1965 a new independent body, the National Board for Prices and Incomes, or N.B.P.I. The N.B.P.I. has no power to impose settlements, or to investigate cases other than those referred to it by government. Nevertheless, it has exercised an influence on management (and, to a much smaller extent, union) attitudes to wage and price movements, and it has helped to influence the climate of public opinion on wages, prices and productivity.

Early in 1966 the government, after much discussion with the two sides of industry, put on the statute book new legislation making it mandatory for wage claims, and proposed price increases in a range of key industries, to be notified to it in advance, so that there would be an opportunity for prior investigation and decision whether on not to refer the increases to the N.B.P.I. before they became operative; this legislation would involve a temporary 'stop' on price and wage increases up to a possible maximum of four months, but no more. This had the effect of bringing the production departments more closely into contact with their industries, since they now found themselves compelled to make rapid assessments of the validity or otherwise of the reasons advanced by firms and trade associations for prospective price increases. The job would have been more expertly done at the outset had the government had more management accountancy resources at its disposal. But the educative effect in Whitehall was nevertheless substantial – and will no doubt grow as time goes on.

The July 1966 crisis broke on the government while this 'early warning' legislation was still going through Parliament. The government was forced to supplement it by stronger measures – a six-month wage and price freeze followed by a further six-month period of 'severe restraint' in which the scope for wage and price rises was severely limited, backed up by legislative sanctions. With the expiry of the government's special powers in July 1967 the long-term form of prices and incomes policy is obscure. It seems plain, however, that whatever happens government must retain an interest in the outcome of individual collective bargaining negotiations as representative of the 'public interest', and also in the movement of prices and non-wage incomes. It must be prepared if necessary to use the weapons at its disposal – e.g., the use of public procurement[4] – to see that prices are not raised unjustifiably.

The issues involved in prices and incomes policy are immensely complex. Any attempt to 'freeze' the price mechanism over a long period would be as disastrous as it would be impracticable. The price mechanism is after all the main way we have of relating supply to demand, and of ensuring that resources (including people, for wages and salaries are themselves a form of price) move to those places where they can be most useful and most productive. An efficient economy requires personal incentives – and it can be argued that in modern Britain we have already gone dangerously far in allowing personal incentives to be eroded, without imposing salary freezes on top of a high rate of personal taxation. Moreover, the cost–price relationship determines the profit ratio, and without adequate profits industry cannot supply the funds to finance adequate new investment – nor pay the dividends which will attract new sources of investment capital. And the profit ratio, or the return on assets, is the best yardstick for managerial efficiency we have.

All this would seem to argue in favour of a wages policy from which prices, profits and non-wage incomes were excluded. But this is an impossibility in political and social terms; rightly or wrongly, neither trade unions nor the general public would accept a 'social contract' which limited freedom of wage determination without parallel restraints on prices and other incomes. Moreover, we have already suggested that British industry on average has too low a ratio of capital to labour. To cheapen labour further in relation to capital would hardly be conducive to raising the standard of industrial efficiency. Indeed, there is much to be said for combining investment incentives with a payroll tax to make labour more expensive (as the Selective Employment Tax of 1966 does for the service trades).[5]

Another argument for subjecting price increases to scrutiny and restraint is that only in this way will companies in general be induced to keep down their costs in a buoyant economic climate. If wage increases are not passed on to the customer, they must be absorbed by increased efficiency. Thus, by making it difficult for firms to pass on cost increases, the government can help to keep down wage increases and/or promote greater productivity.

There are therefore strong economic as well as non-economic arguments for including prices (and therefore profits) as well as non-wage incomes in a policy for limiting wage rises. But the policy must be a flexible one, which does not prevent the price mechanism from functioning effectively. So far as possible the restraints on prices and profits should come from competition, as a function of the overall management of the economy, rather than from government edict. And the objective of the whole policy – on wages as well as prices and other incomes – must be to relate rewards to performance.

Productivity, therefore, in the broadest sense, rather than stability, must be the long-term objective of the prices and incomes policy; the policy must therefore complement rather than conflict with the broad objectives of economic management. Wage negotiations, for example, need to be linked more closely than in the past to productivity agreements and payments-by-results schemes. Productivity bargains on the Fawley pattern are plainly in the national interest. But it is only too easy for such bargains to become a euphemism for an inflationary pay settlement which trades hard cash for promises. Productivity bargains, if they are to yield genuine increases in productivity, require managerial skill and toughness as well as union good faith – and these are not always evident in industry.

The N.B.P.I., in a report on *Productivity and Pay During the Period of Severe Restraint*[6] in December 1966 listed the following requirements for a genuine productivity agreement or payment-by-results scheme:

(i) It must be shown that the workers are making a direct contribution towards increasing productivity by accepting more exacting work or a major change in working practices.

(ii) Forecasts of increased productivity must be derived by the application of proper work-standards.

(iii) An accurate calculation of the gains and cost must show that the total cost per unit of output, taking into account the effect on capital, will be reduced.

(iv) The scheme should contain effective controls to ensure that the projected increase in productivity is achieved, and that payment is made only as productivity increases or as changes in working practice take place.

(v) There should be a clear benefit to the consumer, in lower prices or in improved quality. In some instances, 'lower prices' may mean prices lower than they would have been if the under-taking can prove that factors outside its control would otherwise have led to higher prices.

(vi) An agreement covering part of a plant must bear the cost of consequential increases elsewhere in the plant, if any have to be granted.

(vii) In all cases negotiators must beware of setting extravagant levels of pay which would provoke resentment outside.

It might be argued that the seventh condition, coming on top of the other six, is a work of supererogation, importing as it does considerations extrinsic to the settlement itself – *viz.* its impact on people 'outside' – which negotiators might argue to be none of their concern. But there can be little doubt or dispute about the importance and relevance of the first six conditions.

A fourth essential for viable economic growth, as we have already seen, is an adequate rate of capital investment in indus-try. Investment incentives at the present time need to be both selective and simple. They need to be selective because the type of investment needed is primarily labour-saving invest-ment – investment in plant and machinery rather than new buildings (at least outside the development areas); and because the resources available for investment in industry are inevitably limited. That is one reason for the government's decision at the beginning of 1966 to switch from the system of investment allowances chargeable against tax, applying to most sectors of industry, to a more selective system of cash grants for investment, restricted to manufacturing industry and excluding investment in buildings (outside the development areas).

The second reason for switching from allowances to grants was the evidence that many firms found the allowances too complex to take into account when planning their investment policy, and so failed to take full advantage of them. One of the factors holding back innovation in large sectors of British industry in recent years has, indeed, been a lack of sophistication in the techniques of investment appraisal commonly in use (though it is arguable that as a result of the publicity devoted to the subject industry had just about become aware of the value of the investment allowances by the time they were withdrawn).

According to a report by the Neddy Council, 'many firms appear to apply criteria for assessing investment projects which have little relevance to the measurement of the expected rate of return to the capital invested'.[7] Some firms which distrust their own methods evidently allow themselves a safety margin by pitching their minimum acceptable rate of return too high, thereby turning down investments which could have been profitable.

The simple way of looking at a possible investment is to calculate how much it will earn in a year when fully productive, and express this as a percentage rate of return. In fact, however, costs and receipts are not constant through the life of the investment. Rising labour costs and maintenance charges affect the earnings of an investment towards the end of its 'life'. Costs and receipts should therefore be assessed separately for each year of an investment's expected life.

Another major factor to take into account is the way in which return on the initial outlay can best be calculated. Most companies appear to work on the 'pay-back' period method – that is, by assessing the number of years before the receipts from a project can be expected to equal its initial cost (the time, in fact, before the investment will have paid for itself). This is a reasonable way of assessing the degree of risk of an investment, but it is a bad index of profitability, for it takes no account of the amount an investment may earn *after* it has paid for itself.

The alternative method advocated, by Neddy and others, is the D.C.F., or discounted cash flow technique. Under this method, one begins by calculating the estimated cash outlay (including tax payments) for each year of the life of the projected investment; this one sets against the expected receipts. The difference between the two gives the net cash flow, which has to cover profit and depreciation. But money earned later is liable to be worth less than money currently in hand. Thus the cash flow has to be discounted to allow for this. To take Neddy's example: 'If the cost of capital is put at 7 per cent per annum under the discounting procedure, £107 receivable in a year's time is the equivalent of £100 today.' What one has to do is to establish by trial and error the rate of discount which, applied to the cash flow for each year of the investment, will make the total discounted cash flow equal the initial capital outlay. If the answer is, say, 8 per cent, this is the 'D.C.F. rate of return' – in other words, the investment is expected to earn enough to pay 8 per cent interest on the capital invested as well as recovering the initial investment cost by the end of its life.

Compared with conventional techniques, the D.C.F. approach gives greater weight to profits earned early in the life of the project. The differences can be substantial. One example quoted by Neddy shows that, according to the convention employed, the same investment can be held to yield returns of $1\frac{3}{4}$ per cent, $3\frac{1}{2}$ per cent or $9\frac{1}{4}$ per cent. Not only does the D.C.F. method provide more reliable guidance than the older methods

as to the merits of rival capital projects: it is also a way of deciding whether any investment will yield a return above the
acceptable minimum. The Neddy study suggests that the normal
rate of return on investments in British industry is between
6 and 8 per cent. This is much lower than the rate of 15 per cent
which is normally quoted in industry as the acceptable rate. As
Neddy points out, if the rates expected in industry are unreal-
istically high, investment in labour-saving plant will be
deterred. Thus it may not be enough to make labour more
expensive and capital cheaper. To get businessmen to substitute
the latter for the former, it is also desirable to persuade them to
employ accounting techniques which reflect real relative costs as
accurately as possible. The merit of the D.C.F. system is that it
appears to do just this.

The most important single factor affecting investment decisions must, however, in most cases be the assessment of the
market potential for the products which the new plant and equipment is designed to produce. Too many British firms in recent
years, in assessing the market potential, have tended to think
exclusively in home-market terms, and have not explored as
thoroughly as they might the potentialities of the export market.
Consequently they have tended to under-invest. This has been
particularly true in certain sectors of the engineering industries.
There has been a growing tendency for certain parts of the
engineering industry to rely on sub-contractors to even out the
fluctuations of the business cycle, putting out more business to
them when demand rises and withdrawing it when demand
falls. Since sub-contractors are in many (probably most) cases
less efficient and productive than main-plant operators – otherwise they would probably have graduated out of the risky business of sub-contracting – this means that in boom conditions
engineering costs tend to rise, deliveries to extend and quality
to fall. Hence there is a growing tendency for engineering to
become a bottleneck industry in modern Britain – one which,
unlike the capital-intensive industries of steel, motors and

chemicals, does not operate most efficiently at high levels of demand.

'Stop–go' has also, of course, as we have seen, reduced the total level of investment in U.K. industry and adversely affected its timing, leaving us with serious gaps in capacity – e.g. in chemicals and parts of engineering – which can only be filled at times of high activity by imports. The question of investment timing is of crucial importance, if investment is to act as a stabilizing rather than a destabilizing factor in the economy. It is obviously desirable that investment should be maintained, so far as possible, evenly throughout the business cycle, instead of being overwhelmingly concentrated at the peaks, when capital and labour are already heavily pre-empted and when any extra demand is likely to suck in imports and contribute to inflation. To avoid this two things are necessary. Government must try to avoid 'stop–go' in its policies. Businessmen must learn to take a longer view of the market when planning investments, and not to be over-influenced by short-term movements and changes of sentiment. The establishment of a credible National Plan with a five-year perspective should help here.

## The Use of Resources

More investment is not, however, the only way to raise productivity and cut costs in industry. Existing resources, of plant and manpower, could be used to better effect. There is, for example, considerable scope for more variety control, standardization and rationalization. Compared with many of our competitors, Britain lacks a large home market; indeed, Britain is rapidly becoming the only major industrial power with a home market of less than a hundred million. This is in itself a considerable handicap, but it is compounded by the structure of many of our industries and by the pricing policy of many of our firms. Compared with some at least of our competitors, British industry is remarkably unspecialized. We have a wide range of

firms producing very similar products on what is in many cases
an uneconomically small scale, and even when we do have firms
of international size they tend in many cases to spread their
production over too many products and models. There would
appear to be three main reasons for this. First, Britain is a
relatively protected economy. Our tariffs are high by international standards, while at home competition (in some
industries, though not in all) has been gentle rather than cut-
throat. The result is that firms have not been forced to specialize
by competitive pressures to the same extent as they have in
many other countries. At the same time, the slow and chequered
growth of our economy may have deterred firms from
taking the commercial risks involved in concentrating on a
particular model. To spread one's risks is after all a sound
defensive strategy, more suitable in a static than a dynamic
economy.

But the failure to specialize and to realize the full economies
of large-scale production reflects management failures at least
as much as it does the peculiar features of the national economy.
The willingness to operate on a jobbing rather than a mass production basis is in large measure an indication of timid and
conservative management. In some cases, too, British industry
has not appreciated the cost savings to be derived from concentrating on standard products, because its accounting techniques have been too backward. As a result price structures have
reflected inadequately the extra cost of making and selling non-
standard lines. The Restrictive Trade Practices Act, whatever its
other achievements, has prevented industries from negotiating
collective variety control agreements which would have led to a
better use of capacity. The customer has consequently failed to
appreciate the potential benefit to him of not insisting on unnecessary variety.

What is at fault here is, in fact, a combination of an economy
insufficiently competitive and insufficiently dynamic; of a
management which is insufficiently professional; and of a

marketing policy which is passive rather than active. The jobbing system has been defended on the grounds that it 'gives the customer what he wants'. Yet the most telling point which emerged from the import studies conducted by the Machine Tool and Mechanical Engineering Economic Development Committees (see below, page 128) in 1965 was that imports in this field were being bought primarily on quality, design and specification rather than on price or delivery. The British engineer was losing business precisely because he was *not* 'giving the customer what he wanted'.

There has been plenty of independent evidence, in recent years, that important parts of British mechanical engineering[8] and machine tool production have been tending to become technologically backward. Many reasons have been advanced: poor, unqualified management; lack of adequate status and recognition of designers; unwillingness to take risks; traditional reliance on 'easy' Commonwealth markets; and so on.

I believe myself that another important reason has been the tendency, mentioned above, to rely on sub-contractors as an alternative to investment in new plant. But an even more crucial factor has been what can only be described as a failure of communication between customers and suppliers in many sectors of engineering. In too many cases the customer has not known what the industry could supply, and the industry has not known what the customer wants – or, equally important, is going to want in the near future. Many of the complaints about design inadequacies boil down to the fact that the machine is not designed to do what the customer wants. Both parties are to blame for this: machine makers for failing to carry out adequate market research, customers for failing to take suppliers into their confidence early enough, either through failing to plan ahead themselves or through an exaggerated sense of secrecy. An essential concomitant of national planning needs to be the establishment of better 'planning links' between industries bringing makers and users of British plant and equipment together, so that each can anticipate and meet the needs of the other.

A good deal of progress in this direction has been made by the Mechanical Engineering E.D.C., and by the establishment under Neddy auspices of a special Process Plant Working Party, bringing together the makers and users of chemical, gas and oil plant.

Better use of existing capacity, by greater concentration on long runs of standard products and closer links with the customer, can therefore add appreciably to the efficiency of industry. In some cases, however, this may involve changes in the structure of an industry as well as in the organization of production in individual firms. In some cases the circumstances of the British economy described above have led to an undesirable proliferation of small firms, which lack the resources to sustain adequate R. & D. programmes or to achieve economies of large-scale operation. In others the need is for greater specialization by individual firms, which may require rationalization. To help accelerate necessary adaptations of structure in such cases, without having to wait for the slow and often clumsy and wasteful processes of the natural forces of the market, the government set up in 1966 a special public agency, the Industrial Reorganization Corporation (I.R.C.) with an initial capital of £150 million. The task of the I.R.C. is to promote mergers and rationalization schemes in those sectors of British industry where they appear plainly desirable, and so help to make the structure of our economy more competitive. In the early part of 1967, when the forces of technological change were combining with the squeeze on profits and the decline in markets to intensify the structural problems of many sectors of British industry, the scope for I.R.C. activities as a catalyst of change appeared very considerable indeed.

The other field in which better use of resources is most urgent in British industry is manpower. The National Plan revealed a potential 'gap' between the amount of manpower industry expected to need by 1970, and the amount likely to be available, of around 400,000; and until July 1966 labour shortages – particularly of skilled workers – constituted the biggest single bottleneck hindering further expansion. In present circumstances this bottleneck is likely to recur whenever expansion is resumed. We must, therefore, find ways of using manpower more effectively.

How can this be done? By more labour-saving investment, and by the various measures for better plant utilization listed above; by more effective management policies in general; by greater use of shift work; by measures to improve labour mobility from lower-productivity to higher-productivity jobs; by more effective and more forward-looking manpower forecasting by firms, to identify particular needs and shortages as far as possible ahead, so that measures can be taken to meet them – in particular, by seeing that enough people with the required skills are being trained. Finally, it is obviously of crucial importance that restrictive practices and other man-made obstacles to the most efficient use of labour be tackled plant by plant.

It is impossible to define restrictive practices with precision, or to calculate their cost to industry with any degree of authority. Such estimates as have been made suggest that over the economy as a whole the extent of 'over-manning' (or institutional under-employment) may be between 5 and 15 per cent. That is to say, the current national output could be produced with existing plant and equipment with between 5 and 15 per cent fewer man-hours, given flexibility in the use of labour. In some industries, the proportion is undoubtedly higher.

It is wrong to assume that this under-utilization of labour is primarily due to union obstructiveness. Too often it reflects a lack of awareness by management of the scope for potential labour-saving. The main areas of over-manning are now, however, fairly well known. The most important is probably the insistence on rigid demarcation of the work which different types of craftsmen are allowed to perform, and the insistence on each craftsman having his 'mate'. In some industries union or workshop agreements impose an unnecessarily high ratio of operatives per machine – particularly new machines, which thereby become less profitable to install. In others an artificial labour shortage among craftsmen is imposed through the closed shop and limitations on intake of apprentices. In others there has been successful resistance by craft unions to the 'de-skilling' of jobs through introduction of new equipment. In others, again, unions or groups of workers operate unofficial limitations on piecework by their members, in order to conceal the fact that a particular piece-rate has been set too low. In many industries overtime has become 'institutionalized' in order to push up total earnings: that is, the work is so organized as to ensure that there will be a need for overtime, even if this means deliberate underproduction in normal working hours.

Institutionalized inefficiency in the use of a critically scarce resource is a luxury Britain cannot afford. The problem has been referred to already in Chapter 1, and we will be coming across it again in the next two chapters. Clearly it is something which a policy for faster economic growth cannot ignore. Equally, however, it is one which must be tackled industry by industry and firm by firm. There is no national short-cut, by legislation or administrative edict, which will do the trick.

## The Machinery of Industrial Policy

The measures listed above are by no means a comprehensive list of what is required to enable industry to achieve faster growth. Others are set out in the 'Check-list of Action Required' at the end of Chapter 1 in the 1970 National Plan document, and in the various reports of the E.D.C.s or 'Little Neddies' (see below).

The prime governmental responsibility for industrial performance in general is vested in the Industrial Division of the

D.E.A. The Industrial Division stands, as it were, at the cross-roads between the 'macro' economics of the National Plan and the 'micro' economics of the individual industry and firm. One must never forget that the nation's economy is made up of individual firms and industries, and that growth is what *firms* do. It is no good government drawing up a national plan for growth if the individual concerns lack the will or the means to carry it out. In each industry there are specific obstacles to be overcome if growth is to be achieved – specific bottlenecks or weaknesses. Many of these were listed in Neddy's Orange Book. We have discussed some of the most important in the preceding section of this chapter. There are others which reflect defects in government policy – some general, some bearing on particular sectors of industry; these are instances where government has failed in its 'climate-creating' role mentioned above. But there are others which are indigenous to particular industries or firms, and derive from weaknesses in management, in structure, in industrial relations or some other internal deficiency. Elimination of these obstacles, at the level of the industry or firm, is therefore probably the most important single element in the achievement of a national economic plan.

The D.E.A. Industrial Division falls into two parts. Its main function is to co-ordinate the policy of the various government departments towards industry from the viewpoint of improving efficiency. (Since May 1967 it has also had overall responsibility for prices and incomes policy). It contains, however, in the team of industrial advisers, the biggest influx of high-level business-men into government that Britain has ever known in peacetime. The industrial advisers, businessmen on short-service second-ment from their firms, represent collectively the same mixing of disciplines and experience which, as we have seen, a contract research firm or a management consultant can bring to bear on the solution of problems – but at a rather higher level; for the D.E.A. industrial advisers are typically directors of large companies, in the £10,000-a-year-plus salary range.

The industrial adviser experiment is thus an imaginative – and I believe so far successful – attempt to break down the barriers between government and industry which we have noted before in this book; an attempt to interpret the one to the other, and to improve mutual understanding – and, above all, to enable industrial expertise to be brought to bear on government's thinking on economic and industrial problems before, and not after, the decisions have been taken. It is an attempt to apply in British government the lessons of the French *polytechnicien* and the American 'dollar-a-year' businessman-in-Washington *à la* MacNamara. It is also obviously an extension and application of the Neddy concept of partnership between government and industry. It is an interesting innovation for a Socialist government to have made.

The industrial advisers have two main functions – to advise the government on industrial policy, and to represent the Department on the Economic Development Committees (E.D.C.s) or 'Little Neddies'. The Little Neddies represent applications of the Neddy (hereafter called 'Big Neddy') system at the industrial as opposed to the national level. Like Big Neddy, their membership consists of representatives of management, trade unions and government, with a sprinkling of independents. Their remit is to improve efficiency generally in their industries, as well as helping to draw up and approve the National Plan forecasts for their sectors. The first E.D.C.s were set up during the summer of 1964, and by the time of the October election nine were in operation and several others in process of formation. The secretariat for the Little Neddies, as for Big Neddy, was provided by the Neddy Office (N.E.D.O.), and each Little Neddy contained one N.E.D.O. member. The government side was represented by the sponsor department for the industry (usually the Board of Trade) and the chairman was an independent.

Up to October 1964 the E.D.C.s had achieved little, and in some cases they appeared to be in danger of degenerating into

'talking shops'. Like Big Neddy, they lacked any kind of executive authority, though the fact that they contained representatives of leading firms and trade associations in their industries
implied a greater likelihood of successful 'follow-through' than
Big Neddy, with its broader field, could expect. But the chief
problem was a lack of any central direction. The Little Neddies
had been set up, but nobody had really told them what was
expected of them or how to do it. Big Neddy was in decline after
the failure of the bid for an incomes policy and the apparent
divergence of the economy from its planned targets. The
Treasury lacked the knowledge, and the production ministries
the drive or enthusiasm, to remedy Neddy's lack of leadership;
and the coming election cast its shadow over everything.

After October 1964, when the D.E.A. took over sponsorship
responsibility for the Neddy organization from the Treasury,
the Little Neddies acquired a considerable fillip, and their
position in the general scheme of things became very much more
important – not least in relation to the Neddy Council, whose
role and status had clearly been affected by the removal of the
planning function to D.E.A. The industrial advisers, working
closely with the Neddy Office, have played an important part in
guiding the work of the Little Neddies. By the end of 1966 the
number of Little Neddies in operation exceeded twenty, and
their span covered the bulk of the labour force in private industry. There was one E.D.C. in the public sector, dealing with the
Post Office, and a highly effective 'functional' as opposed to
'industrial' E.D.C. dealing with the movement of exports. Most
had established a number of sub-committees and working
parties.

The programme of work for each E.D.C. has naturally varied
with the nature and problems of the industry. Nevertheless, some
common priorities have emerged. To begin with, each E.D.C.
was asked to examine the export–import balance in its industry
(this remit was in fact given *before* the 1964 election), and to
suggest ways in which it might be improved. This, and the work

involved in drawing up the industrial chapters in the National Plan, provided useful catalysts, revealing the main problems which needed to be tackled.

From then on the work of the E.D.C.s has become increasingly varied, though in most cases it has tended to revolve around the items in the Plan Check-list and the problems listed in the preceding section of this chapter. Nevertheless, in the degree of priority given to each subject, and the method chosen for tackling it, each E.D.C. has tended to vary – and there has also, not surprisingly, been considerable variation in performance and achievement, ranging from the significant to the imperceptible.

In general, up to the beginning of 1967 more progress had been made on problems of structure and organization than on manpower utilization. The Electrical Engineering Little Neddy has devoted much effort to trying to reduce product proliferation. Early in 1966 an agreement was concluded between the cable manufacturers and the electricity area boards which aimed to reduce the number of mains cables in use from over 250 to around 27, and similar agreements have been under negotiation in other parts of the industry. Rationalization proposals which would drastically reduce the number of competing units have been discussed for distribution transformers and meters, and others are under consideration as this book goes to press. Structural problems are particularly important for an industry like electrical engineering, where the large firms tend to be multi-product concerns and where there is a proliferation of small units, and where the public sector in the shape of the nationalized industries buys about a third of total production.

Other E.D.C.s have given priority to other problems. Mechanical Engineering has concentrated on the establishment of maker–user liaison committees with its main customers. The Machine Tools E.D.C. is working on a detailed action programme to improve competitiveness and increase capacity;

others are concentrating on ways of reducing imports and improving exports. Others, like Distribution, with an immense and fragmented industry to cater for, have tended to act more as propagandists for greater efficiency, putting out booklets on stock control, on the use of labour and the more efficient handling of goods, and so on. All E.D.C.s have been hampered at various stages in their work by two main factors: by gaps in statistics (slowly being remedied), and by the enormous problems of communicating effectively with their industries – particularly in those sectors where there is not a strong trade association system.

In trying to evaluate the success of the Little Neddies in their first two years of life, it is important to remember that – like the regional boards and councils which we shall consider in the next section – theirs must be a long-term impact, and one which can probably never be quantified. At best, the removal of obstacles to growth is likely to involve a whole series of useful but unspectacular measures (the variety reduction exercise in cables is a typical example). Had the Little Neddies not existed, it would almost certainly have proved necessary to create them – for without an organization linking government and industry at industry level, economic planning can hardly be effective. The E.D.C.s provide at least the beginnings of a bridge between the state and the individual enterprise. They enable economic policy to be adjusted to the individual needs of individual industries, rather than trying to fit all industries into the same Procrustean bed of policy. Moreover, the fact that they have a definite commitment to efficiency and growth – to change, in fact – sets them apart from the 'established channels' through which the dialogue between government and industry has traditionally been carried on (i.e. the network of trade associations and similar bodies and the sponsor department in Whitehall), where the weight of vested interests must inevitably be great.

At the same time, there is a danger in trying to extract more from the Little Neddies than they can give. The place where decisions are taken in industry is still pre-eminently the board-room of the individual enterprise. Not only have Little Neddies as such no executive authority over their industries; their members are not even, in the strict sense, representatives empowered to negotiate. Indeed, E.D.C.s are not really negoti-ating bodies at all. They are primarily media for communication and cooperation. I believe that much more thought needs to be given to building effective channels of communication between the E.D.C.s and the grass roots of industry. But there is also a need to see that government policy is actively directed towards achieving the kind of objectives to which the E.D.C.s have been giving their attention, and remedying the deficiencies which their work has been bringing to light.

One way of doing this is to induce, by legislation, a greater amount of information about company performance. A start has been made on this in the 1966 Companies Act. If one is to exam-ine efficiency one must be able to measure and to compare – to compare best and worst in an industry, and with other industries and other countries; in this way one can assess standards of performance, and provide management with bench-marks against which to test its own achievements in particular fields, and the degree of efficiency with which assets are employed. One way of doing this is by use of the techniques of inter-firm comparison. The Centre for Interfirm Comparisons, a non-profit making body sponsored by the British Institute of Manage-ment, has done some useful work in this field. More elaborate comparisons can be done by management consultants. But use of these techniques is less general in British industry than it should be, and too many managements still lack the essential statistical material to enable them to assess their own performance and that of their subordinates. Consequently one finds remarkable discrepancies, in such fields as manning ratios for particular jobs, in the return on capital in particular operations, in the rate of stock-turn, and so on, between firm and firm and even between different sectors of the same firm. It has been often said that the variation in standard of performance between best and worst in British industry is among the widest in the world. This is partly the product of a comparatively easy economy and a tolerant society which enables mediocrity to survive, but it also reflects the lack of sufficiently rigorous standards of comparison. At present too much of the effort to improve business efficiency from outside is a species of blind man's buff. It is therefore, in my view, highly desirable for government to insist on fuller disclosure of information about business performance, so that the standards and methods of the best companies can more rapidly be filtered down to the others, and those that cannot match them can be induced – voluntarily or otherwise – to quit the field.

A second major contribution which government can make towards raising industrial efficiency is through the more purposeful deployment of public procurement – including the procurement of the nationalized industries and local authorities. The scope for manoeuvre here is somewhat more limited than may appear at first sight. Many of the purchases of the public sector are prescribed by the particular circumstances of the transaction, and there is a limit to the extent to which any public purchaser can be encouraged to forgo a commercial bargain in order to help forward a particular policy. Nevertheless, public purchasing *can* be used to promote variety reduction and structural rationalization (as the aircraft and heavy electrical manufacturers know full well), to help boost innovation and exports, as well as to provide special assistance to firms in development areas and as a tactical weapon in prices and incomes policy. In France public procurement, the granting or withholding of industrial development certificates, and the allocation of priorities in access to the capital market, have all been used to considerable effect in inducing industry to co-operate in the objectives of the national plan. Without going as far along this road as the French authorities, I believe we could do more to encourage better industrial performance than we have hitherto, through the strategic and tactical use of public procurement – *provided*, and this is crucial, that the priorities and their relative weight (as against each other, and as against normal commercial criteria) are defined clearly in advance.

There are many other things government can do to improve the industrial climate. Some are set out elsewhere in this book. Some are very general in their application. For example, I believe that many of the problems about the structure of British industry which have been discussed above may be radically eased if we succeed in our bid to enter the European Common Market. This would give us the large market and the competitive spur which we at present lack. Others are much more specific. But the prime need is to give industrial efficiency *as such* a higher rating in our policy priorities, and to accept the implications thereof. If this were followed through literally, the changes in particular aspects of government policy would be very radical indeed.

## The Role of the Regions

One of the main problems in economic policy-making in the United Kingdom is the contrast between the basically over-heated areas of the Midlands and South, and the largely under-employed regions in the North and West. Action to damp down inflation in the former is liable to create excessive unemployment in the latter before its object is achieved, and the creation of full employment in Scotland and the North has in the past only been achieved at the cost of unsustainable pressure of demand in the more fortunate regions further south.

It follows that, until a better balance can be established between the various regions of the United Kingdom, action designed to create full employment without inflation through the orthodox measures of fiscal and monetary policy applied nationally is likely to be self-defeating. We need to plan much more systematically than in the past to ensure that a larger-than-average proportion of new national growth is steered to those regions with the spare capacity to absorb it. (This is of course the rationale behind proposals for regional variations in the application of Selective Employment Tax.)

In the past government policy towards regional development has tended to proceed on a spasmodic *ad hoc* basis, concentrating on giving special incentives to new industries to go to those areas which could show a high rate of unemployment. In the early post-war years these areas were broadly defined. In the mid-fifties the concept switched from the broad aim of regional regeneration to the much narrower, more specific one of filling in pockets of unemployment. This entailed drawing the boundaries of those areas which would qualify for special treatment much more narrowly. The beneficiaries under the new policy tended to be individual towns rather than whole regions or districts. When the unemployment ratio in a particular town fell below the critical figure (typically 4 per cent) it was normally removed from the list.

The trouble with this policy was that it treated the symptom and not the cause. The object of regional policy is not to try to plug particular unemployment holes wherever they may appear, but to try to create within each region the basis for viable self-sustaining growth. If a town cannot normally qualify for special treatment until unemployment has already manifested itself, it is not in a position to plan ahead for future unemployment, to ensure a smooth redeployment of labour. This was the case with the North-east at the end of the fifties, when the slow run-down simultaneously in the order books of the shipyards and the labour requirements of the coal mines created a virtual certainty of heavy unemployment, which in fact materialized two years later. This was foreseen in the region, and had there been an effective comprehensive plan for regional development the unemployment might have been averted. As it was, the pre-planning to meet the expected unemployment was on too limited a scale.

Second, the limiting of special incentives to particular areas of high unemployment tends to freeze the labour pattern, and to prolong artificially the life of towns and areas which on every count of commonsense should have been allowed to die a natural death – at the expense of the natural growth areas of the region, with better industrial and social facilities and potential. There is little rational justification, for example, for trying to preserve an area of worked-out coal mines by equipping it with new factories in preference to a much more attractive and viable new town twenty miles away. The 'infilling' policy – whatever its political attractions – tends to ignore the increasing mobility of the modern car-owning worker as well as the economics of indus-trial location.

Third, the industries liable to be attracted by the policy of the short-term bribe are not necessarily those most suitable to their new locations. (This is an argument against regional employment premiums.) This is a problem from which all the development areas have suffered. If unemployment is high, there is clearly a strong case for accepting any industry which will come. On the other hand, it is clearly preferable to create a complex of indus-tries which will generate its own growth rather than have a heterogeneous range of factories which lack natural links and which draw the bulk of their supplies and sustenance from other areas. Northern Ireland provides an example of a region which has tended, since the war, to accumulate new industries magpie-fashion, without any clear organic links between them – without, therefore, providing much opportunity for the invest-ment of local capital in service facilities or backward or forward integration. (There are however some signs today that the synthetic fibre factories established in Northern Ireland may provide such a natural nucleus for organic growth.)

A rather more purposeful attempt to generate new growth was the drive, at the end of the fifties, to provide central Scotland with a motor-car industry. The British Motor Corporation and Rootes were persuaded to build new plants in Scotland, and Colvilles was induced to build a steel strip mill to supply them.

(The economics of this operation, which was backed by a government loan, do not bear too close an examination.) But in this case, though the concept was good, the success hoped for has proved elusive. The local Scots firms have shown themselves very slow in setting up the kind of network of component and accessory manufactures which keeps the Midland motor firms supplied. This looks like a failure of local enterprise, which is slowly – too slowly – being remedied. Until it is, the Scots motor plants will be too dependent on parts bought in at high transport cost from England to be fully competitive, and unless a bigger outlet for its steel materializes in Scotland the Colvilles strip mill will be too heavily dependent on markets outside Scotland – where it has to compete against Welsh strip mills with a much shorter haul – to be fully competitive itself. Here we have a classic example of a vicious circle, due to an imaginative attempt at a coherent regional development project having gone off at half cock. And if one asks why it went off at half cock, the reason seems to be that the importation of alien industries – so long as the centre of decision-making remains outside – can only go a certain way towards helping an under-developed region achieve 'take-off'. The missing element is local enterprise.

What conclusions should one draw from this? First, regional development cannot be conducted in a short-term, piecemeal fashion. Nor can it concern itself solely with mopping up isolated pools of unemployment, nor ignore the overriding need for industries to be located where they can operate to maximum efficiency. What is required is a balanced regional plan for development, relating needs to resources, and the objectives and requirements of each region, not only to each other, but also to the nation. (It is absurd for a single region to plan its develop-ment as if it were a self-contained economy.) This is the task of D.E.A.'s Regional Policy Division, which took over responsi-bility for regional planning after the 1964 election from the Board of Trade.[9] The existence of the regional division illus-trates the axiom, which those of us who were concerned in drawing up the blueprint for the D.E.A. came to feel acutely, that the planning function is really indivisible: that a viable growth plan must concern itself, not only with economic planning strictly defined, but also with planning at the industrial level, planning of incomes and prices, and – not least – land use planning in the broad sense.

Each region now has a regional planning council, composed of leading local employers, trade unionists, local authority representatives, and so on – and a regional planning board, consisting of government officials. Their job is to draw up and ensure coordination in the implementation of regional development plans, within the context of the National Plan – and also to co-ordinate the policy of different government departments towards their regions. The board comprises the regional representatives of all the ministries which have a regional structure (Board of Trade, Labour, Housing, Technology, Agriculture, etc.), under the chairmanship of a member of the D.E.A. It is the D.E.A.'s job to reconcile the various regional plans to each other and to the National Plan. (In Scotland, Wales and Northern Ireland the position is of course somewhat different, since the first two have their own ministries, the third its own government; but the structural principle remains the same.)

It is clearly desirable that there should be some means of ensuring that different government departments are not carrying out mutually contradictory policies in particular localities – withdrawing railway services, for example, from areas to which the Board of Trade is trying to attract new industries. And it is probably true that in the past there was excessive centralization in London of decision-making affecting the regions. The Conservatives started the trend towards devolution of decision-making in the special case of the North-east before they left office. Advocates of regional devolution argue that under the present system the regions have more of the semblance of authority than its substance, that the leading-strings are still held too firmly in London, and that for this reason the experiment in regionalization has been a sad disappointment.

I believe there is something in this criticism; but there is another side to the story. Where there are conflicting claims between regions – as is inevitably often the case – the final decision must be taken centrally. Only the central authorities can decide in the last analysis where the main *national* growth-points of the future should be located; the prospective development of Humberside and Severnside as cities of the future is being planned in the D.E.A.'s Central Planning Unit in Whitehall. And any move towards a major devolution of decision-making runs up against the snag that the regional councils are not elected bodies. The long-term solution may well lie in the rationalization of the structure of local government, to create a handful of major units large enough to carry out the kind of functions now performed by regional councils, but with the added advantage of being elective organizations. This would permit a more radical devolution of decision-making. It is to be hoped that the Maud Committee currently considering the structure of local government in England and Wales will report in this sense.

In the meantime, however, it is fair to say that the respective roles of regional planning councils and national government in regional development need to be clarified. It is also true that wherever the responsibility may lie, successful regional planning requires that the objectives be defined in each case. Curing unemployment may be one of these, but it is unlikely to be the only one. In the Midlands and South-east the main problem is rather one of physical congestion and overheating. That these are problems of affluence rather than of poverty does not make them any less important – or any less intractable. In Scotland the economic problem for many years expressed itself in low productivity rather than high unemployment (the unemployment came later, as an inevitable consequence). In some other regions unemployment is masked by a high emigration rate. In many regions the industrial base needs to be widened, and in almost all the social infrastructure needs to be modernized and improved.

Improvement of the infrastructure is indeed essential even for the limited objective of attracting new industry. This is one of the most important lessons of regional development learned in the early sixties – and for this, as for many other insights into this whole problem, the nation is particularly indebted to the bright young thinkers and planners of the Scottish Council.

If a firm is to go to a new area, it needs to know, not only that it will be able to get workers, but that they will be of the right sort. In fact, development in some regions – e.g. the North-east and Northern Ireland – has been held up in some cases by critical shortages of skilled workers and technicians, at a time when unskilled workers were queueing up for jobs. This same problem has been encountered on the Continent, notably in Southern Italy and the more backward areas of France. This is one reason why it is so important for a region to hold on to its skills, and not to lose them all by emigration. It follows that one of the best ways of attracting new industries is by having good training and education facilities.

Education is a key factor in other ways too. New firms will need technologists and managers. If these can be acquired or trained locally, so much the better. If executives are brought in from outside, they will want good local education facilities for their children. If they cannot get these, they may not be willing to come no matter what the financial inducements. And if a firm cannot persuade its managers or technicians to move, and cannot recruit enough locally, it cannot move itself.

There are other factors which will crucially affect a firm's decision to move to a development area. The need for good access to markets and raw materials is obviously fundamental. Hardly less so is the need to overcome the problem of divided management. Perhaps the biggest worry confronting firms deciding to set up branches in new areas is the question of managerial control. In almost every business the scarcest available resource is executive talent. If a firm sets up widely dispersed branches, does this mean that the managerial team will need to be increased so that each branch is under direct supervision, or will the existing team try to exercise control over more units than before? Clearly the answer to this question – and therefore in many cases to the firm's ability or willingness to move – will depend to a great extent on the efficiency of communications. It follows that a good transport system is an essential attribute of a viable development area.

Moreover, business executives, like other men, do not live by bread alone; still less do their wives. The quality of housing, of shopping and entertainment facilities, of leisure activities, indeed the whole quality of life, will influence to a profound extent the willingness of business executives to bring new enterprise to a development area. In all these ways, therefore, it is vital for a region wishing to attract new industry to build up its social infrastructure. This is one reason for trying to concentrate new industry in natural 'growth points' where these services can most readily and economically be provided. Indeed, achievement of the National Plan not only requires a faster rate of growth in the under-developed regions than elsewhere. It also requires that the proportion of public expenditure in these regions on a per capita basis should be greater than in the others. To describe such expenditure as 'unproductive' is plainly misleading.

But the relationship between the quality of life and the attraction of new industries (which means new executives, technologists and technicians) is not a one-way process. Experience has shown that the injection of this new social element into a previously conservative and socially stratified society creates new demands and a new attitude, which permeates fairly rapidly through the community. This in itself is liable to raise the quality of life, through the incentives and the pressures which it creates. Markets are created for new types of products and services not formerly in demand – for example, executive-type houses in Scotland, supermarkets and boutiques in Ulster. Educational standards and facilities are likely to be particularly affected by the demands of the incomers. So the initial arrival of new industry may help to create the kind of climate in which other new enterprises may flourish, and in which local enterprise can expand to supply the needs – material and spiritual – of the incomers.

How can this leaven be made to work more quickly and thoroughly? This is the question now concerning the theorists of the development areas. How can one create, in a formerly backward area, the 'take-off' situation in which growth becomes self-generating instead of having to be fed in by periodic injections from outside, at considerable cost and effort? How create a situation in which new industries no longer come because they are bribed to do so, but because they want to – or where they are no longer needed anyway?

In this situation it is the new, science-based industries which inevitably come most closely under scrutiny. These are the industries with the most obvious growth potential, the equivalents for the next decades of the motor, oil and chemical industries in the post-war era so far. Moreover, in contrast to these they are to a considerable extent footloose industries, in that they do not require huge investments of initial fixed capital, nor is their location obviously affected by predetermined physical factors of access to mass markets, raw materials and components, or fresh water. Today's development areas suffer from the fact that in the main they failed to attract the new industries which developed between the wars and immediately after 1945, and consequently are still far too dependent on the older industries established before 1914 – coal, shipbuilding, natural textiles and so on; and this is a weakness, not only because these are in many cases declining industries, but because in too many cases also outmoded ideas and relationships have become embedded in the fabric of the older industries.[10] It is obviously highly important for the development areas that they should get a reasonable share of the industries of the future such as electronics, nucleonics, the manufacture of computers and automation equipment, and so on.

Here, again, American experience is instructive. At the beginning of the fifties I spent a year teaching economics at a New England university. At that time the industry of the region was dominated by old and declining industries – notably cotton textiles; and the centre of the textile industry was in any case moving to the Southern States where labour was cheaper and less unionized. The industrial future of the Boston hinterland looked bleak. When I revisited the area three-and-a-half years ago it was transformed. Boston and its immediate hinterland contained the biggest concentration of electronic and other science-based industries in the world, and these industries had taken the leading place in the area. (Today Boston's claim to primacy is contested by similar concentrations in the areas of Palo Alto in California and the Space Centre at Houston in Texas.) What had caused this transformation?

The answer is provided by the existence in the Boston area of what is probably America's biggest concentration of high-level institutes of advanced education headed by M.I.T. and Harvard, together with an exceptionally large number of research institutes, including Arthur D. Little. Consequently there is a very high turn-out of technologically-trained graduates, and these are precisely the people needed by the science-based industries. The amenities of Boston and of the New England countryside make the area an attractive one for intellectuals, so that it was not difficult to persuade these people to accept jobs in the neighbourhood – particularly if these jobs enabled them to maintain access to the research laboratories of M.I.T. and elsewhere. As a result firms wanting to expand in the science-based sector of industry found it convenient to come to the Boston area in order to exploit the talents of the science and technological graduate expertise available. Moreover, many local research workers started to pursue work with apparent commercial implications. They therefore began in many cases to set up their own business organizations to develop their discoveries, closely linked to the research laboratories and institutions whence they had sprung. By the mid-fifties what has been called 'a critical mass of research-based companies' was operative in the area – at least ninety of them (including the biggest, Raytheon) founded by M.I.T. alumni or faculty members.

The greatest concentration of these new industries is along Route 128, a 65-mile highway which runs in a semicircle to the west of Boston. At the time of my first stay there it was a quiet country road of poultry farms, with land selling at around $1,000 an acre. When I went back land prices had jumped more than thirty times, and more than $150 million of industrial plant was installed in new electronics, nucleonics and other factories along its length. Greater Boston today boasts more than five hundred electronics firms alone, nearly half of them along Route 128.

The government has helped by steering a substantial proportion of the R. & D. work on defence and space projects to the area. When Massachusetts had a president in the White House it was better placed in this respect that it is today, when Houston, Texas, seems to be doing rather better in the securing of new R. & D. contracts. But the government came to Greater Boston essentially for the same reason that industry did – that here was an exceptionally good supply of the raw material that it needed.

What has happened in the last decade in Greater Boston is a test case of the economics of regional development in the automation age. In this age the key material for economic development is going to be, in my opinion, an adequate supply of well-trained technologists, research scientists and the like (plus an adequate supply of risk capital). And institutions like M.I.T., which can provide this expertise, are likely to play the same sort of role as coal mines and water power in the first industrial

TI—F

revolution. The industries of nineteenth-century Britain were established, predominantly, on and around coalfields. The science-based industries of late-twentieth-century Britain will be built, in the same degree, around technological institutes and centres of higher learning.

It is no accident that in the United States today almost every sizeable community is trying to establish its own research institute on the model of Battelle or Stanford, as a means of attracting new industry and averting a local 'brain drain'. The success of the Palo Alto complex in California, which enjoys access to Stanford University and Research Institute, as well as proximity to California's great aerospace industry and the well-known attractions of Californian life, teaches the same lessons as Route 128.

Nor is this phenomenon of universities and research institutes becoming nuclei for self-sustaining industrial growth in their localities confined to North America. In Israel the world-famous Weizmann Institute at Rehovoth, which is an institute of pure research, when I visited it two years ago, showed signs of having learned the Boston lesson. Some small science-based enterprises had set up in Rehovoth expressly in order to provide commercial outlets for the research discoveries of the distinguished occupants of the institute. This is potentially of great importance for Israel, a country which suffers from a small home market and high labour and transport costs for its products, and which therefore needs to concentrate its export efforts on goods with a very high value-added content.

What are the implications of this for Britain? It is disturbing, but hardly surprising, to find a very high proportion of Britain's science-based industries in South-east England. This is not only because this is the part of Britain where most technological graduates probably prefer to live. It also contains most of the nation's research institutes and laboratories, and a substantial proportion of the biggest and best universities. Finally, and perhaps most important, London is the centre of government;

and government, in Britain as in the United States, is the main purchaser of science-based equipment and the main sponsor and financier of research. Access to government is therefore of crucial importance to the science-based industries.

What can the development regions do to reverse this centripetal tendency for tomorrow's industries? One thing that can certainly be done, as part of the investment in the social infrastructure of the regions, is to try to create some equivalents of M.I.T. It is a pity that neither of the first two graduate business schools is in a development region. This should be rectified in the second round of creation of business schools. The long-projected technological university on Tees-side should be given a high priority. An extremely interesting development is the project, jointly fathered by the Scottish Council and the Ministry of Technology, for trying to build a science-based industrial complex at the new town of East Kilbride, using the National Engineering Laboratory and the new University of Strathclyde as the research base. This is a conscious attempt to reproduce in Scotland the conditions which brought success in Greater Boston, and if it succeeds it is likely to prove a pilot project for other development regions.

A critical factor in this kind of development is the relationship between the academic institutions and industry. We have already seen how important it is in the diffusion of technology for there to be the maximum cross-fertilization between different sectors of society, the minimum of rigid compartmentalization. We have already seen that Britain has tended to be weak in this respect. Nowhere has this been more true than in the relations between education and industry. This may be one reason why the United Kingdom has excelled (particularly in contrast to the United States) in basic research, but has fallen down on applied research or technology. Where inventions have been successfully applied in British industry, the lead time has often been unnecessarily long.

We shall look at this problem again in its general industrial context later in this book. But here it is worth pointing out that the British universities must themselves bear a large part of the blame. British education has traditionally been dominated by the humanities, and by pure as opposed to applied science. British universities have tended to hold themselves aloof from industry. We have seen that, in contrast to American universities, they have been extremely slow in introducing any form of business studies into their curricula. M.I.T. and other large American universities have long run well-staffed industrial liaison departments to keep businessmen informed, not only about the courses they run, but about the research projects which are under way and their possible industrial implications. Now, led by Manchester, British universities are starting to set up similar institutions.

In the United States, and in this case also on the Continent, it is common practice for scientists and engineers to divide their working week between university and industry – in some cases doing consultancy work for various businesses, in some cases as employees of a particular company. In the past this division of effort has been frowned on by British universities, and although the practice is growing it is still regarded with disfavour by some of the older and more snobbish universities. Yet, as we have seen, it is precisely by such an interplay between university and laboratory on the one hand, and industry on the other, that technological progress is made.

To build up technological growth centres on the Boston, Palo Alto or East Kilbride model requires, therefore, full co-operation from the universities of the area concerned. In the past Scottish education has been even more obscurantist than English in this respect – both in its stiff-necked attitude to co-operation with industry and to allowing its staff to take on consultancy work, and in its reluctance to install computers. It is to be hoped that the new universities will have different ideas.

This is particularly important in Scotland's case, because this is one development region which already has a good sprinkling of science-based industries – including computers, automation, data-processing and control instruments, micro-circuitry and so on. There is here an encouraging nucleus on which to build. And this is one part of the United Kingdom where the American 'spin-off' technique for diffusing technology has actually worked – partly as a result of the 'Joint Electronics Scheme' pioneered by Sir John Toothill of Ferranti in the mid-fifties.

Ferranti's Edinburgh factory has always been deeply involved in defence procurement contracts which probe the frontiers of technological knowledge. During the late fifties, with government blessing, a number of self-contained, specialized teams of scientists and technologists were built up within the framework of various Ferranti contracts; and subsequently each of these was grafted, as a going concern with sub-contracts of its own, on to one of the interested local firms.

In this way the state was able to help indirectly in the diffusion of technology, if in a modest way. Toothill and his Scottish colleagues have since argued that a further step could be taken along the road if more of the agencies of government – particularly procurement offices – could be moved into the regions. In the long run the idea of a separate political capital in the northern part of Britain (such as the *Economist*'s 'Elizabetha'), leaving London as the commercial, financial and social capital, will have to be taken very seriously indeed. I believe we should start to study the economic, logistic and other problems involved now. And if one is thinking of a second capital, the claims of Edinburgh clearly demand attention!

A more modest move, the decentralization out of London of a number of government agencies, is already under way. The Ministry of Technology in particular has shown itself aware of the importance of such moves. Regional development could be further helped by the movement of more research association laboratories, and some of the defence procurement agencies, out of southern England. Such moves, plus the generous investment incentives already provided, may in time enable the less-developed regions to acquire in their industrial anatomy more 'brain' as opposed to 'brawn' – a greater proportion of the new, activating type of industry, and a greater proportion too of the executive and highly qualified type of business manpower: a 'brain drain' in reverse in fact, which will enrich the life of the regions in more ways than the purely material.

The problem of decentralizing R. & D. is not just a British one. The United States is not happy about the dominance of California, Boston and Texas in this field, while the French government is making a deliberate attempt to promote research activities in the area of Grenoble to counter the attraction of the Paris area, which today contains 70 per cent of all R. & D. personnel in France. An even more radical attempt at decentralization is being made in the U.S.S.R. In 1957 more than 70 per cent of Soviet scientists and engineers engaged in R. & D. in academy institutes were working in the Moscow and Leningrad regions, and 40 per cent of all research institutions were in or near Moscow. A massive attempt is being made to create a rival pole of attraction for technologists near the remote Siberian railway town of Novosibirsk, home of the Siberian Academy of Sciences. Here the Russians have built an experimental satellite town, Akademgorodok, devoted exclusively to scientific and technological research and to providing the technological infrastructure for the industries of this formerly backward region. Today Akademgorodok has a population of 50,000, with eleven major scientific institutes, a university, and a very generous array of social services and educational provision. It is, in fact, the 'Eggheads' City' par excellence. The Russians seem to be trying to reproduce by deliberate policy the conditions which produced the apparently spontaneous generation of science-based industry in the Boston area. No experiment of equivalent daring is taking place in this field anywhere else in the world, and the success or otherwise of the Novosibirsk complex – and so far it does seem to have been broadly successful – is therefore of enormous interest.

Certainly the regional machinery in the United Kingdom has not so far thrown up anything one tenth as adventurous or ambitious. Indeed the achievements of a systematic policy for regional development in this country still lie in the future. So far the planning councils and boards in the regions have been finding their feet and sorting out their priorities. The new machinery will take time to work. But the fact that it is there is important. It is in the regional machinery that the requirements of physical and economic planning can be fused and reconciled. And if there is to be a meaningful dialogue between government and the individual enterprise, the regional channel of communication is likely to be as important as the industrial channel through the E.D.C.s and N.E.D.O. The nation, after all, is the sum of its regions.

## The Travails of Technology

Original plans for the D.E.A. included responsibility for ensuring the rapid application of the benefits of modern technology to industry – a subject which had bulked very large indeed in the Labour Party's propaganda in the twelve months prior to the October 1964 election. Shortly before the election, however, it was decided to entrust this function to a new, separate ministry – the Ministry of Technology. After a shaky start, this ministry now looks set to become one of the most powerful stars in the Whitehall firmament.

To consider the role of the Ministry of Technology it is necessary to go back in time a few years. There had been a growing suspicion for some time after the mid-fifties that the organization of scientific policy was defective. The establishment after the 1959 election of a Ministry for Science did little to alter this feeling, for the Ministry had very limited resources and made little impact. In 1963 three separate reports on the subject appeared. A Federation of British Industries working-party report on ' Civil Research Policy' argued for more R. & D. expenditure by both state and industry, with greater co-operation between the government research establishments, industry's research associations and private firms. It took a critical view of many of the smaller research associations and urged that there should be amalgamations, with a number of different research associations to be grouped on a common campus so that certain facilities could be pooled, and the benefits of large scale more readily obtained.

The F.B.I. report also concerned itself with the question of broadening the government's support for technology from its heavy concentration on the defence industries. It urged that all government departments should be allocated funds so that they could place development contracts on their own authority with private industry for their own purchases. Where the government was not itself a buyer, the F.B.I. urged that innovation should be promoted by identifying areas of promising research and allocating grants-in-aid for R. & D. projects in these fields, on the basis of shared costs. The proper criterion for a government-supported project should be one where the benefit accruing to the national economy was greater than that accruing to the individual firm concerned; in such cases 'the government should not be over-sensitive about possible advantages which might or might not accrue to the company to whom the project has been entrusted'. Normally, however, the government might expect to receive a royalty on sales made from the results of projects it had supported.

The government was urged to be more ruthless in its choice of firms to receive grants-in-aid, and not to shirk 'the possibly invidious task of selecting the most suitable firm on the basis of the best chance of success' – in a word, not to be afraid to discriminate.

The F.B.I. recognized that its recommendations would require an increase as well as a redeployment of scientific manpower, and it concerned itself also with the appropriate form of governmental organization. It suggested that 'the Minister for Science must bear responsibility for determining the allocation of state support as between all these claimants and for the scientific strategy on which it should be based'. In this he should be assisted by an advisory council including representatives from industry. The actual allocation of funds within this broad strategic framework should be the responsibility of a steering board, linking representatives of government, industry and the universities, which would advise the Minister.

Finally, the F.B.I. urged that the National Research Development Corporation (N.R.D.C.), which operated under the aegis of the Board of Trade, should be encouraged to be more adventurous in its support of speculative inventions and developments, like the Hovercraft, by being given greater financial latitude.

A report by P.E.P. (Political and Economic Planning) in July 1963 on *Government's Role in Applying Science to Industry*, called for 'a greatly extended and systematized programme of civil development contracts and "earmarked" grants integrated with a national economic plan coordinated by the N.E.D.C.', to 'achieve a technical breakthrough in those key industries where Britain has fallen behind its competitors, and help to overcome the "development gap" which at present delays the transformation of a project from a prototype to actual production on an economic scale'. This would call for a relaxation of the financial controls imposed on civil development contracts and greater capital reserves for the N.R.D.C.

The P.E.P. report stressed the need to improve the dissemination of information about technology, and urged the establishment of a team of technically qualified 'salesmen' to visit firms and explain relevant scientific innovations in laymen's language. This should be made the responsibility of the D.S.I.R., which should also take steps to see that its research stations improved their publicity services. To help finance the extra expenditure involved in the P.E.P. recommendations, the report urged that there should be an expansion of the system whereby research associations in certain industries are financed by a compulsory levy of firms in the industry. To link innovation with national economic growth, P.E.P. called also for a technical–economic arm to be established at Neddy.

October 1963 saw the report of the Committee of Enquiry into the Organization of Civil Science, under Sir Burke Trend.[11] The Trend Report recommended a major reorganization of the complex network of mutually independent establishments dispensing government money for science and their replacement by a group of interdependent research councils, covering medicine, agriculture, science, and natural resources respectively. This would involve the dissolution of the D.S.I.R. A new autonomous Industrial Research and Development Authority was proposed to take over responsibility for most of the D.S.I.R.'s research stations, together with the industrial research support work carried out through the D.S.I.R. and the whole of the work of N.R.D.C. All these bodies would report to the Minister for Science, who would also acquire added responsibilities for allocation of funds for civil scientific R. & D. The Ministry for Science would, for the first time, become an effective force.

In fact, what happened was that the Ministry for Science was merged with the Ministry for Education, which already of course was responsible for the universities. The post-Trend reorganization was still under way when the election took place and the Ministry of Technology was set up.

The new post-election system divided responsibility for research between pure and applied science, the former remaining with the Department of Education and Science, the latter going to the new ministry, which also took over the N.R.D.C. from the Board of Trade. The Department of Education and Science thus retains responsibility for a range of research councils, embracing medicine, agriculture, 'natural environment' (geology, hydrography, oceanography) – natural resources having gone to the Ministry of Land (subsequently merged with Housing) – and science (astronomy, space, university nuclear research etc.). Research work done at the universities falls, of course, within the sphere of influence of this ministry.

The Ministry of Technology took over the bulk of the research stations from the now-defunct D.S.I.R., the National Physical and Engineering Laboratories, the Atomic Energy Authority, the N.R.D.C., and responsibility for development contracts in private industry and for the sponsorship of industry's own research associations (which are partly government-financed). In addition, and more controversially, it took over from the Board of Trade and Ministry of Aviation sponsorship functions for a group of key industries – machine tools, computers, electronics and telecommunications. This decision met with much criticism. It was argued that it inflicted an unnecessary further blow to the prestige of the Board of Trade, already suffering from the establishment of the D.E.A. as a new power in the industrial field and from the loss of its regional responsibilities to this new department. Second, it was argued that being a new department without a well run-in 'machine', Technology was less well-equipped than the Board to perform sponsorship functions.

The third and most fundamental criticism of this decision was, however, that it involved a confusion of function. The job of the Ministry of Technology, argued the critics, was, like that of the D.E.A., a general one – to speed up the rate of technological innovation in British industry, and to formulate and carry out a strategy for the application of the limited resources available in the best way. If the ministry were at the same time given responsibility for particular industries, it would be tempted to devote more energies to these than to others outside its empire, and this could conflict with the requirements of a national strategy for technology.

As against these arguments it was claimed, decisively, that a ministry without specific industrial responsibilities would be too like the old Ministry for Science, and probably not much more effective. The criticism has instead been met by giving the

Ministry of Technology more industries to sponsor rather than less. The engineering industries were transferred to it from the Board of Trade at the end of 1965, shipbuilding at the end of 1966, and at the beginning of 1967 the Ministry absorbed the Ministry of Aviation and its responsibilities for the aerospace industries. The implications of this trend for national policy are examined in the concluding section of this chapter.

The Ministry of Technology started its life with some important disadvantages. It had been heavily 'over-sold' in advance, and the difficulties of mounting a national strategy for the better application of technology were not widely enough understood. It did not, as did the D.E.A., spring as it were fully-armed like Pallas Athene from the brain of Zeus. The ministry has suffered until recently from staff shortages and its reach has persistently tended to exceed its grasp. Insufficient prior research had been done to define its priorities or to map out the most effective organizational structure. The structure has in fact had to be changed several times, but it now looks to be assuming a sensible form.

Indeed, after a discouraging start the Ministry of Technology now seems to be finding its feet, and it is legitimate to expect faster progress from now on. Apart from the Advisory Council on Technological Policy – which advises the Minister directly on broad policy questions and corresponds to the research councils at the Department of Education and Science – the ministry is divided into three main groups. One of these is the former Ministry of Aviation. The second is the Engineering Group, which carries out the ministry's sponsorship functions towards the industries (excluding aerospace) in its charge. It is jointly headed by a civil service administrator and an engineer, and sub-divided into ten sections. Five of these deal with sections of the engineering industry, as follows:

(1) Electronics, telecommunications and instruments;
(2) Computers;

(3) Machine tools and manufacturing machinery;
(4) Vehicles and mechanical engineering products;
(5) Shipbuilding, electrical and chemical plant.

The other five divisions deal with general questions not specifically related to particular parts of the engineering industry. These cover, respectively:

(1) Standards (including responsibility for metrication);
(2) Economics and statistics;
(3) Information and regional work;
(4) Productivity services, exports and international technological cooperation;
(5) General industrial problems – including public procurement, I.R.C., the supply of technologically qualified manpower, etc.

These ten divisions are staffed by teams of mixed background and disciplines, blending professional administrators, scientists and engineers. One important aspect of the diffusion of technological information for which this group is responsible is the Industrial Liaison Service, which operates on a regional basis and provides on-the-spot advice to industry on technological problems, thus helping to meet the need for technical 'salesmen' identified in the 1963 P.E.P. report. The Industrial Liaison Officers are grouped under nine regional centres, which are based on Colleges of Advanced Technology (C.A.T.s) and Technical Colleges. Their work is particularly oriented towards smaller firms, and links in with the regional organization under the D.E.A. described in the last section. Other measures designed to bring technology to the small firm are the new Advisory Service of the Production Engineering Research Association (P.E.R.A.) and the ministry's Low-Cost Automation project, for extending automatic control in firms or for purposes where heavy expenditure is not required or feasible.

The third group, the Research Group, is headed by a scientist and controls the tools with which the job of technological innovation may be expected largely to be carried out. The main resources at the disposal of this group are the ten government research stations formerly run by the D.S.I.R., the seven Ministry of Aviation research and development establishments, the Atomic Energy Authority, the N.R.D.C. and the 47 industrial research associations which receive government assistance.

So much for the ministry's organization. Before examining its achievements, it is worth looking again briefly at the problem – or rather problems – which require solution. There is, first, the problem with which, as we saw in Chapter 3, the United States has been grappling somewhat unsuccessfully: namely to ensure a wider diffusion of technology from the advanced industries to the less advanced. In Britain there are, however, two further problems – to raise the *general* standard of technological awareness, which is a much more acute problem here than in the United States; and to see that a greater proportion of the nation's technological input goes to help right the export-import balance, which is also a much more serious problem for Britain than America. There is also the need to reduce the lead time between invention and commercial application.

In the United Kingdom, as in the United States, most research is state-financed, and most state-financed research goes to industries which contribute to the defence programme. These industries account for three fifths of the government's R. & D. budget, and two fifths of the nation's. In 1958, research expenditure represented 35·1 per cent of the net output of the British aircraft industry and 30·9 per cent of the American. For electronics the figures were 12·8 per cent and 22·4 per cent respectively; for metal products, 0·8 per cent and 1·3 per cent; paper, 0·8 per cent and 0·9 per cent; food, 0·3 per cent and 0·5 per cent; textiles and clothing 0·3 per cent and 0·2 per cent. It will be seen that the situation is broadly parallel between the two countries, and that the research content varies very much more between industries than it does between countries (the all-industries figure being 3·1 per cent for Britain against 5·7 per cent for the United States).

The same point can be made another way. In 1962 the aircraft industry accounted for 38 per cent of R. & D. expenditure in U.K. industry, but for only 4 per cent of U.K. exports. Mechanical and electrical engineering accounted for 24 per cent of Britain's exports but only 17 per cent of R. & D. A given value of aircraft exports, it was calculated at that time, incorporated sixty times as much research expenditure as the same value of ship and marine engineering exports, and fifty times as much as the same value of motor-car and railway exports.

The situation has not changed basically since then. There is the same need for some central organization to coordinate the country's scientific effort and to establish the criteria for priorities. (Guidance on this latter point can be expected from the recently established Advisory Council on Science and Technology under Sir Solly Zuckerman.) This, as in the case of the individual firm, involves trying to assess the potential return on a piece of research expenditure in relation to the possible alternatives; this calculation including, not only the likelihood of the research yielding important technical results, but also the potential social and economic as well as commercial implications. Given that there will always be more potential projects than resources available, the appraisal techniques required need to be of great sophistication and the risk element must be high. Nevertheless, the techniques and the approach required are essentially the same as those we examined at the 'micro' level in the American context in Chapter 2.

In deciding where the government's own contribution should be made, priority should be given – as mentioned above – to those areas where social benefits exceed those which would accrue to individual firms. There are many reasons why private industry, left to itself, would tend to under-spend on research. Some scientific achievements are likely to be non-marketable (e.g. the results of research on noise or pollution). Others, like research on health, exports or conservation of natural resources, are of direct benefit to the community. In other cases, individual firms may be too small to reap the full benefits of research – or even to be aware of the possibilities.

On the other hand, from the community's point of view there may well be a waste of research, due to duplication between firms (too many computer types, or the Central Electricity Generating Board's tendency to duplicate research being done by the electrical engineering firms), excessive product differentiation (in detergents or toothpaste for example, or some of the other excesses of the U.S. 'new products' vogue), or work undertaken without adequate economic assessment or knowledge of what is going on elsewhere.

In other words, social costs and benefits can diverge from private ones quite as markedly in the field of R. & D. as in other economic activities, and these divergences must be taken into account in planning a national strategy for innovation. Such a strategy must also seek to foresee those areas in which major breakthroughs may be possible, and the particular bottlenecks which are likely to impede progress – institutional obstacles, obstacles due to the size and structure of firms, the pattern of ownership, taxation and other government policies, defects in design, shortage of scientists and research facilities, lack of technological awareness and education, and so on. It must also investigate ways of improving the 'fall-out' on civil technology from defence expenditure, which in Britain as in the United States has tended hitherto to be somewhat disappointing.

Next, a strategy for technology must examine the relative advantages in particular cases of conducting research oneself or of importing 'know-how'. As the costs of R. & D. mount, it is becoming increasingly clear that there is going to have to be more international specialization and trade in 'know-how' as in other things; this applies particularly to the smaller industrial countries, like the Western European states. This need is apparent both in the civil and the defence field.

Finally, a strategy for technology cannot become a strait-jacket in which everything is pre-planned, nothing left to chance. Room must be left for the flowering of creativity, wherever it may occur. A strategy for innovation is, in a sense, an exercise in 'planning the unplannable'. Innovation cannot be commanded; it must be encouraged and coaxed.

It will be seen that this exercise is among the most difficult and delicate that can be undertaken in a modern state, and it is one which no country has mastered so far. What progress has the Ministry of Technology made towards it?

To the outside observer, there does not seem to be much sign as yet of the emergence of a grand strategy. And some at least of the weapons at the ministry's disposal have proved less potent than had been hoped. Allocation of funds to promote R. & D. projects has been hampered by the need to contain government spending. The extension of civil development contracts, widely advocated as a panacea before the 1964 election, has proved rather more difficult to put into practice than expected. Suitable candidates have proved disappointingly rare, and the question of finding an eventual purchaser for a successful civil development project has not proved an easy one to answer. The extension of public enterprise in areas of lagging technology has not so far been applied, and one doubts if it is a likely runner in the immediate future on any large scale – not least because of the shortage of available top-level technologically qualified management who could be expected to make such enterprises a success. On the other hand, the possibility of partnerships between the state and private enterprise to develop new techniques or products should not be ruled out, and there might well be scope for public enterprises or 'mixed enterprises' to exploit the products of civil development contracts unable to find a normal commercial outlet. Equally, the I.R.C. is an obvious means of creating industrial structures capable of exploiting and promoting technological advance – e.g. in telecommunications, machine tools, electronics or in some sectors of engineering. It would be wrong to rule out the extension of public enterprise, in pure or mixed form, as a means of accelerating technological advance or overcoming particular capacity bottlenecks in the British economy in future years.

In the short term there is scope for the more systematic use of public procurement to encourage innovation. Not much progress has yet been made in this field. There is a need for closer cooperation with the Ministry of Defence, if the enormous purchasing power of the state in the aerospace and other defence fields is to be used more purposefully to boost civil technology, and if the service departments are to be weaned away from their traditional 'one-off' mentality in equipment ordering. There is also a case for more prototype purchasing, or some specific tax incentive to offset the special costs of innovation. (The Mechanical Engineering E.D.C. has suggested a special 'innovation grant' to the first purchaser of an item of equipment which embodies a recognized technological advance.) The ministry has done something in this field, notably through the use of pre-production contracts for numerically controlled and other advanced types of machine tools, but not yet as much as its critics would like.

At the same time, progress is being made, if in a somewhat piecemeal manner. The N.R.D.C.'s borrowing powers have been increased from £10 million to £25 million, and its terms of reference broadened. The total value of projects submitted to it in 1965–6 was ten times greater than in the previous year, and it now has more than 120 development projects to its credit. In addition to well-known projects like the Hovercraft and Dracone – both now at last at the commercial production stage – the N.R.D.C. is doing a considerable amount of work on computer and automation systems (with International Computers and Tabulators, or I.C.T., and Elliott-Automation), machine tools and various chemical projects, among others. It has recently developed a £1 million scheme for buying numerically controlled machine tools and leasing them out to prospective users on terms which allow the machine to be returned for cash at any time between six and twenty-four months after installation. The main job of the N.R.D.C. is to bring projects from the laboratory to the commercial stage, and its work is therefore in many ways central to the whole function of the Ministry of Technology.

The Atomic Energy Authority is being encouraged to diversify into non-atomic R. & D. projects, and a start has been made on desalination, metal-shaping and medical research work. Considering the scientific resources available in the A.E.A., this diversification will need to go much further and faster if the Authority is to justify the size of its establishment.

The work of the ten specialized research stations and the 47 cooperative industrial R.A.s is being reappraised and in some cases reorganized. The National Physical Laboratory is working on special programmes concerned with measurement, the National Engineering Laboratory on numerically controlled machine tools and automatic design techniques for engineering, and so on. Some research associations have been encouraged to do special work on variety control, instrumentation, etc. All useful work, though a good way short of the scientific revolution we were led to expect in 1964.

The ministry has been giving a good deal of thought to ways in which the work of the research stations and R.A.s could be better coordinated. It is not yet clear which way its thinking is going, but there is plainly room for improvement if the nation's considerable effort in the field of industrial research is to produce a better and quicker pay-off.

With the absorption of Aviation, the Minister of Technology now controls the biggest concentration of resources for advanced technology in the world in relation to the size of the country. The department has a total payroll of some 36,500 and an annual gross expenditure of around £750 million. It employs some 9,000 qualified scientists, engineers and technologists – 5,000 in the A.E.A., 2,000 in the ex-D.S.I.R. research stations and a similar number in the former Ministry of Aviation R. & D. establishments. Of these over 8,000 are engaged in R. & D. work. (Comparable figures for private manufacturing industry are about 120,000 and 37,000 respectively.) The ministry buys over £300 million of aircraft, missiles and electronic equipment a year, and is responsible for nearly half the nation's total expenditure on R. & D. (some £325 million out of an estimated £750 million a year). There is therefore an enormous responsibility on the minister and his officials to see that these resources are effectively used.

It is widely argued in industry that the accumulation of scientists and technologists in the A.E.A. and government research stations is excessive, and represents a wasteful use of a critically scarce resource. There is some substance in the argument that salaries of government scientists have been allowed to get out of line with those payable in private industry, so that they have no incentive to move out of the public sector even when their talents might be better deployed in private industry.

This problem might be met in various ways. The most radical, and possibly the least satisfactory, would be simply to close down or drastically shrink a number of government research stations and release the staff to private industry. An alternative might be to let out more government research work and government research teams to private industry on contract. Another alternative would be to release much more information about the research work of the government stations and try to work more closely with industry in exploiting the commercial implications of such research. There is undoubtedly room for greater interpenetration and cross-fertilization between government and industry in the R. & D. field; and a first requirement if this is to take place is to break down the barriers of secrecy which have tended hitherto to enshroud the work of the government research establishments.

### Technology's Children: Computers and Others

As time has gone on, the ministry has come to seem less and less of a Ministry of *Technology*, and more and more of a Ministry of *Industry*. The ministry's concept of its sponsorship functions has been very different from that of the traditional production ministries – notably the Board of Trade. Its attitude towards the industries in its bailiwick is a much more active, interventionist, dynamic one than has been normal in Whitehall. Like the D.E.A., it believes that it has a mission to solve problems and accelerate change in its industries; its philosophy in this respect is not unlike that activating the Little Neddies. In the last eighteen months it has been steadily acquiring the resources to realize its ambitions.

The importance of government policy for the development of the science-based industries is illustrated by the sections of the National Plan contributed by the Electronics E.D.C. and the Scientific Instrument Manufacturers Association. The former points out that the government can help technological advance:

(a) by setting an example as a buyer, e.g. by setting techno-logically advanced specifications;

(b) by fiscal incentives for the installation of advanced machin-ery;

(c) by treating current expenditure on R. & D. including the development of computer software, in the same way as investment in plant and machinery for tax purposes.

On the organization of R. & D. work, the Little Neddy wants this to be contracted out to industry as far as possible in those fields where the government is the prime or sole purchaser. Also, where R. & D. is done within the government, it argues that this should not be tied narrowly to military requirements, but phased in so far as possible with a common R. & D. policy worked out in collaboration by government and industry.

On the impact caused by changes in government require-ments, the E.D.C. comments that 'British industry needs as much advance warning as possible of the specification and design characteristics required by the government'. The scientific instrument makers point out that 20 per cent of their output goes to the public sector, and better liaison is needed between firms and government so that the necessary R. & D. work can be initiated at the earliest possible moment. They also urge that government development and production contracts should wherever possible be to specifications drawn up to take account of non-government user requirements, to get the maximum 'spill-over' effect.

The first major industrial problem to confront the Ministry of Technology was the future of the British computer industry. This was a test case of the kind of industrial problem which is going to be increasingly common as technology advances. It is a particular example of the economy of large scale, of the advantages which can be derived from massive technological inputs which can be backed up, where the breakthrough occurs, by large-scale production, marketing and servicing. In the industries where these circumstances obtain – in computers, aircraft, missile and weapon systems, rockets, automation equipment – the individual nation is rapidly becoming too small a base to sustain a viable industry. As the costs of R. & D. escalate, and the risks increase on the frontiers of knowledge, this dichotomy between the resources of the individual nation and the technological input required is likely to mount. Cases of this kind are likely to prove among the most difficult for the politicians of the late sixties and seventies to solve.

Britain is now the only non-Communist country outside America with a viable native computer industry.[12] Outside Britain the only non-U.S. firms still designing and developing their own equipment on a significant scale are those making small scientific computers or specialized installations. These include, for example, Brown Boveri, Telefunken and Philips. But so far as general computers are concerned, all the formerly independent Continental manufacturers of any size – Olivetti,

Siemens, Machines Bull – have now either merged with U.S. interests or manufacture American machines under licensing agreements (as does Saab in Scandinavia). A rump independent French computer industry comprising three firms struggles on with government support, but it is of marginal importance – and probably of marginal commercial viability.

One single U.S. company, International Business Machines (I.B.M.) controls more than two thirds of computer production in the non-Communist world, and Britain and Japan are the only major countries on this side of the Iron Curtain in which it accounts for less than half the total market. In the United States I.B.M. has some half-dozen competitors, some of whom – notably General Electric and Honeywell – have followed it into Europe. The terms on which the leading Continental producers have had to accept partnership with these U.S. concerns means that the 'know-how' and the R. & D. content are mainly centred in North America.

This U.S. dominance applies in other sectors of electronic capital goods – in radar and navigation aids, telecommunications, industrial process control etc. – as well. In 1963 and 1964, according to the *National Institute Economic Review* of November 1965, the United States accounted for 75 to 80 per cent of world production of all types of electronic capital goods, and for two thirds of world output if one excludes defence equipment. It also accounted for 60 per cent of world exports of such goods. These figures do not include the production of U.S.-owned companies outside North America, which are estimated to account for 15 to 20 per cent of all electronic capital goods output in Western Europe.

The reasons for the American lead are interesting and far from obvious. In most types of electronic capital equipment, the original discoveries were made in Europe; this was true, for example, of radio, radar, television and computers. But the United States was much more successful in cutting the lead time from discovery to commercial production, and in the provision of 'software' and peripheral equipment which made the 'hardware' commercially attractive. Factors in this success were the quality and scale of R. & D. investment, the skill and determination of management, the availability of finance, and the assistance and stimulus provided by the huge U.S. defence (and, subsequently, space) budget. Other important factors were the U.S. technical lead in the development of components and the capacity of U.S. firms, partly through ability to deploy massive resources, partly through business flair and advanced production planning techniques, to move with extreme speed into quantity production once the technical and commercial problems were overcome.

At all events, during the nineteen-forties and early fifties U.S. firms built up a commanding position in this field – or at least in most sectors of it. In fact, however, U.S. dominance is far from total. In radar and navigational aids, Britain and France between them have about a third of the world export market, and in the United Kingdom Decca and Marconi have been particularly successful – despite the fact that 90 per cent of total world demand is concentrated in the United States. The world market for electron microscopes is dominated by Siemens of Germany, Associated Electrical Industries (A.E.I.) of Britain and four Japanese firms. European (including British) firms account for 40 per cent of world exports of broadcasting equipment. And in industrial process control – or automation – equipment, despite the fact that U.S. companies control about four fifths of the world market, three British companies – Elliott-Automation, Ferranti and English Electric – have nevertheless managed to acquire an important 'corner'; between them they account for about 13 per cent of world installations. This partly reflects the special concentration in this field of Elliott, and partly the European lead in electronically controlled machine tools acquired by Ferranti. The biggest problem facing these companies until recently has been the conservatism of the British customer (*vide* the situation reported towards the end of

Chapter 1, as pp. 39–40) – which may of course also reflect defects in the commercial approach of the manufacturers.

However, in recent months there have been indications of a marked quickening of interest in British industry. Process control equipment still accounts for only 10 per cent of the total computer market, and there is estimated to be a seven-year time-lag between the development of business data machines and automation equipment. But the market is currently expanding at a rate of 40 per cent a year, twice as fast as the overall computer market. Process-control installations are going in fast into power stations, chemical works, steel and paper mills and other industries, and a similar increase is taking place in the installation of numerically controlled machine tools. The British manufacturers are certainly going to have to face increased U.S. competition in the next few years, and there may well have to be some reduction in the number of British process-control computer manufacturers; there are some half-dozen in the field at the moment. But there is little doubt that a viable British industry can be maintained.

In the general computer field, however, the picture has been much less reassuring. The two British manufacturers are I.C.T. and English Electric (formerly English-Electric-Leo-Marconi) which is strongest in office computers. I.C.T., which competes directly with I.B.M., has been through a sea of troubles in recent years. Nevertheless, though only a tenth the size of I.B.M., it is still possibly the second largest computer manufacturer in the world. For some years I.C.T. and I.B.M. each held about a third of the British market, but in 1964 I.B.M., with its new 360 range, began to pull ahead.

It is obviously not easy for companies of the size of I.C.T. to compete effectively with I.B.M. The U.S. giant spends as much on research alone as most of its rivals do on all their activities put together. The scale of its production facilities means that it can get the benefits of mass production in a way which its competitors cannot; and it can also outstrip them on servicing. Moreover,

I.B.M. has perfected the system of standardized 'hardware' and 'software' or peripheral equipment which can be adapted to customer requirements, thus combining the advantages of variety reduction with flexibility.

Nevertheless, I.B.M. is not invulnerable, as has been shown by the way in which some of its smaller U.S. competitors have been increasing their share of the home market recently at its expense. Britain's comparative weakness in the computer field has been partly due to the conservatism of British management, partly to the failure of the computer manufacturers in the past to appreciate the importance of salesmanship. There has been an undue concentration on hardware at the expense of software; the engineer has tended to dominate the marketing man. The computer has been regarded too much as a glamorous and expensive piece of office equipment or industrial machinery; not enough as a fundamental tool of management, which – if it is to pay its way – must involve a radical change in the whole conduct of operations by the computer user.

At the end of 1964 the writing seemed to be on the wall for I.C.T. The government had three choices. The first was to do nothing, to rely on market forces, and accept the risk that this could mean, in a fairly short time, the extinction of the native industry. Whether or not one can accept this with equanimity depends on one's overall strategy for innovation, which I discussed above. One cannot protect every technologically advanced industry from competition, nor should one lightly deny British industry access to the best available equipment, wherever it comes from. On the other hand, if one regards the British computer industry as viable in the long term, and if one regards computers – as there is every reason for regarding them – as such a crucial element in the complex of science-based industries that their disappearance from this country would critically retard the growth of technology as a whole, then there plainly is a case for considering some form of protection. (The point here is that the computer is the focal point of automation systems.

Research on computers also has great 'spill-over' potential for other science-based equipment. It follows that when one talks of the need to preserve a native computer industry, it is the managerial, R. & D. and design element that one needs to keep here, not just the construction facilities for the hardware.)

The Ministry's decision in fact was to provide financial support to help I.C.T. develop its software, to encourage the spread of computer centres for British equipment, and to give a very wide margin of preference to British computers in public sector purchasing. Development contracts have been placed by N.R.D.C. with I.C.T. and Elliott-Automation, and a number of research contracts have been placed with universities for work on aspects of computer technology. The government has accepted the Flowers Committee recommendation that £30 million should be allocated to universities and similar institutions to buy research computers, but it is spreading these purchases over a longer period than the five years recommended in the Flowers Report.[13] It is also setting up a National Computer Centre, which will help particularly with the drawing up of computer programmes for individual users. It is looking into ways of reducing the initial cost of computer installations, and of helping firms to undertake the initial research needed to determine the feasibility of installing a computer. The Post Office is to set up an electronic data processing or 'computer grid' service, which will give companies access to computer time without putting them to the expense of buying or hiring their own.

The long-term effect of these measures remains to be seen. But in the short-term they have undoubtedly been successful. This is largely because of the coincidence of four factors. First, the British computer market – which, as we saw at the end of Chapter 1, was lagging up to 1964 – suddenly 'took off'. British computer installations in the last few years have been growing at a faster rate than in almost all other major countries, and are now in line with those of other Western European countries. At the same time I.B.M. ran into serious difficulties with its 360 model, and I.C.T. and English Electric came up with new hardware systems which are technically at least the equal of I.B.M.'s. Indeed, the English Electric 'System Four' model is technically probably the most advanced in the world, embodying as it does a switch from transistors to printed micro-circuits – a revolutionary leap forward with implications which will be discussed below.

Finally, the British computer manufacturers have begun to make headway in the software field too – both as regards data processing and process-control equipment. Computer centres have been established where potential customers, operators and programmers are taught the use of computers; there is a new emphasis on peripheral equipment, on the development of satisfactory computer languages and so on. Elliott have developed a modular system of computer-controlled automatic process equipment, in which the various elements can either operate as self-contained units or as part of an integrated system controlled by a 'hierarchy' of computers. In this way the customer can buy his automation in small units, rather than having to take the plunge in one enormous splurge of capital expenditure; the initial outlay can be approved by the production engineer, instead of having to go to the boardroom for sanction.

As a result the British computer industry now looks in better shape than it has for many years. But it is much too soon to say that the danger is past. With its enormous resources I.B.M. can ride out periods of temporary difficulty in a way in which its smaller competitors cannot. In particular there must be some doubt about the long-term ability of the United Kingdom to continue to maintain two separate general computer manufacturers. There would seem to be a strong case of using government influence – possibly through the I.R.C. – to arrange a merger between I.C.T. and English Electric at the first appropriate moment. (See the Postscript, p. 275).

The other point which needs to be made is that the decision to protect British computers was one forced on the ministry by circumstances, and not necessarily part of a comprehensive strategy for innovation. It is hard to envisage any such strategy which did *not* include computers as one of the growth points for development; but a strategy confined to computers alone would be unsatisfactory. Mr Freeman and his colleagues in the *National Institute Economic Review* of November 1965 suggest two other candidates: industrial automation and process-control equipment (because, as we have seen, Britain has already built up a fairly strong position in this field), and teaching aids (because of the current and prospective shortage of teachers); in the latter case they propose a National Centre to provide information and consultancy and to promote R. & D. and an accelerated university research programme into software aspects of learning systems. (Some universities, including Sussex and Sheffield, are already active in this field.)

In both Britain and America there has been a marked tendency recently for electronics and publishing enterprises to join forces to develop the programmed learning, audio-visual systems and other fields of educational technology. In the United States Xerox, I.B.M. and most of the other computer companies are active in this field, and in the United Kingdom I.C.T. and N.R.D.C. are involved, among others. With the expansion of education, and the growth of technical training arising from the work of the industrial training boards (see Chapter 7), teaching aids look like providing one of the main growth markets for the application of electronic equipment in the next few years.

Two other priority candidates in the electronic field may however be mentioned also. One is telecommunications, where the predominant buyer is the Post Office. This is not a field in which Britain has been exactly a world leader in recent years, despite the achievements of individual firms. But with the impending switch from electro-mechanical to electronic equipment, after some fifteen years' development, the industry is on the verge of a radical transformation; and there should be major spill-over from electronic telephone exchanges to other fields of tele-communications and control. This is an area where more dynamic procurement policies by the Post Office can play an important part in accelerating technical advance. The I.R.C. is currently investigating the structure of this industry.

Another crucial sector is micro-circuits, which are replacing transistors in the latest generation of computers. As we have seen, the English Electric 'System Four' is the first computer in the world to make the full leap in components from transistors to micro-circuits; it can only be a matter of time before others follow suit, for the micro-circuit represents as great an advance in speed and compactness over the transistor as the transistor did over the valve. For tomorrow's computer technology, there-fore, micro-circuitry will be absolutely crucial.

Yet in this field the Americans, largely because of their space and defence programmes, are several years ahead of the rest of the world, both as regards the scale of their operations and the state of their technology. At present the United Kingdom imports more than half its micro-circuits from the United States. There are two British firms operating on a substantial scale – Ferranti and Marconi (part of the English Electric group). Elliott-Automation is building up its output, and Plessey, A.E.I. and Mullard are undertaking or planning to undertake manufacture.

Investment in this type of production is expensive and risky. Two questions arise. Can the U.K. market support six domestic manufacturers (compared with four in the vastly bigger U.S. market) or will some rationalization be necessary? And can any British firm or combination of firms hope to stand up to American competition over the next few years? It seems likely that sooner or later the Ministry of Technology is going to have to take a strategic decision on the future of the micro-circuit industry in Britain.

Any kind of technological strategy is going to involve officials in taking deliberately discriminatory decisions between firms –

in 'backing horses'. This is in many ways a new departure for British civil servants, not readily accepted; but, given our limited resources, inescapable. And, in the N.R.D.C., the ministry has an agency which is used to taking such decisions. Also, it is clear that if we are to realize our full technological potential – not just in meeting U.S. competition in Britain but in developing export markets – structural changes are going to be needed. In nuclear power station construction, in computers (both data processing and process control), in telecommunications, in micro-circuits and in some sectors of instrumentation there is a clear case for greater concentration and rationalization to get the best use out of our limited resources. The scope for I.R.C. activity in the technological field is therefore considerable.

In the nuclear field, where despite Britain's technological lead the export record of the private nuclear consortia has been poor, the ministry is promoting a reorganization which involves a pooling of resources between the A.E.A. and the best elements in the private consortia. This should end the duplication of resources which has been going on hitherto, and lead to greater concentration of effort on a smaller number of designs.

However, the options in the field of technological policy – whether one is talking of computers, of aerospace, or any other kind of equipment – are not limited to national protectionism or *laisser faire* fatalism. The third alternative is to try to build up international industries which can exploit the benefits of large-scale operation on a basis of partnership across national frontiers. In some cases this partnership might be with the United States. But, because of the huge American lead in most sectors of technology, such agreements are likely to be one-sided – and in most fields the natural base is likely to be European. This is likely to become an increasingly important option in the next few years. Preliminary talks have taken place with the French authorities on possible fields for joint development; candidates that have been mentioned include a big scientific computer (though this now looks unlikely), fuel cells and a hovertrack rail system. It has been clear for some time that Europe could only enter the space 'race' on a supra-national cooperative basis, and the current booster rocket programme (which is not, unfortunately, going particularly well) is in fact a tripartite Anglo-German-French project. The same principle is being applied to certain types of advanced weapons systems, though the degree of cooperation here has hitherto been less than satisfactory. In the long run I believe the European N.A.T.O. countries will be forced to accept a joint European Defence Community, with an Anglo-French nuclear arm and a combined procurement agency which would place orders on a *European* basis. Otherwise the European defence forces will end up either totally dependent on the United States for their sophisticated equipment or else dangerously under-equipped, or both.

The United Kingdom has had to face the consequences of a 'go-it-alone' policy on defence technology in recent years, and after an agonizing series of failures seems now to have accepted its limitations. France, with a stronger domestic economy, a greater sense of nationalistic pride, and a rather better legacy of skill or luck in recent years, has yet to face her moment of truth. But all the signs suggest that her time, too, is coming, as development costs mount and the pay-off recedes. The fact is, not that the British or European failure rate is proportionately much higher than the American, but that the margin of error we can allow ourselves is so much smaller. We have to put more of our eggs into one basket because we have fewer baskets to put them into. We cannot afford to spread risks as the Americans can. We have to gamble more heavily on the success of fewer projects. Moreover, if the Americans *do* succeed in a design they have two great advantages over us. They appear to be able to move much more swiftly from prototype to full production stage – for reasons which have been suggested above. And the large size of their home market makes it easier for them to cut unit costs. Not all these advantages are a function of size and national income, but some are; and these can only be overcome if the European nations are prepared to pool their efforts.

What is true of defence and space equipment applies, of course, equally to commercial aircraft. The Anglo-French decision to undertake joint development of the 'Concord' supersonic airliner was an historic one, whatever the merits or demerits of that particular aircraft or of the way in which the contract was drawn up. The 'air-bus' project for a high-density short-haul airliner now under discussion between the two countries and Western Germany looks *prima facie* a somewhat more attractive venture. But even here the commercial margin for a viable non-American enterprise looks painfully small. (Other Anglo-French joint ventures in aerospace include the Martel guided missile, the Jaguar strike-trainer aircraft a joint helicopter programme, and the projected variable-geometry strike intercepter aircraft for the 1970s.)

The 1965 Plowden Report on the British aircraft industry[14] spells out in detail the economic facts of life facing this industry. It documents the enormous advantage enjoyed by U.S. firms in being able to cover development and 'learning' costs by longer production runs, on both civil and military aircraft, due to the size of the home market. For aircraft introduced into service between 1955 and 1961 the average production run for U.S. military aircraft was three times as long as ours, for transport aircraft four-and-a-half times as long. The result was that U.S. production costs – despite higher labour and material costs – averaged 10 to 20 per cent less than ours, and the buoyant home market for U.S. aircraft provided a much stronger base for exports. Britain's position has been further weakened by defects in government purchasing policy and weaknesses in management, marketing policy and structure in the leading aircraft firms themselves. But the basic problem has been the limited home market, and the limited resources that could be devoted to aircraft production, which left little room for manoeuvre in the event of commercial or technical failures.

The Plowden Report opts therefore for a positive attempt to build up a European aircraft industry consisting of the British, French, German, Dutch and Italian industries – together with any others who may wish to come in and have something to contribute – which would aim to meet Europe's basic needs, while relying on the United States for projects where the development costs are very large in relation to the market. 'We do not think', says the Report, 'it will ever be worth while for a British manufacturer to embark alone on a new long-range aircraft, or on any new aircraft that is particularly large or complex. On the other hand, it might be reasonable to embark in cooperation with partners in Europe on an aircraft with one, or even two, of these three characteristics.' The Report also makes a number of recommendations as to ways in which the government could help the industry by a more enlightened and far-sighted procurement policy, which would encourage spill-over from defence projects, and help forward planning and exports. The Report also reveals, incidentally, that in 1965 the United Kingdom was already a party to three international production agreements and 25 international development agreements or projects in the aerospace field. Four of these agreements were with the United States, six with Germany, ten with France, five with Benelux or Commonwealth countries and three with international organizations (N.A.T.O. and the two European space agencies). The habit of international collaboration has therefore taken hold in this field.

The Plowden Report has been criticized, with some justifica-tion, for not going deeply enough into the problems of the British aircraft industry; these, indeed, deserve a book in themselves. But the basic logic behind the Report's recommendations is nevertheless sound. A country of Britain's size can only maintain a viable aircraft industry by extreme specialization, or by exceptional skill and luck. Since these cannot be guaranteed, the solution must be to rationalize the industry and rebuild it on a supra-national basis where it can command a Continental market and Continental resources. And what is true of aircraft or computers today is going to be true of a widening band of industries – not excluding motor cars – tomorrow, as the scope of technology and the economic advantages of large scale (not, as we shall see in the next chapter, unconnected) become more and more evident. The forces which drove Britain in the early sixties to seek a place in the European Economic Community have received a further impetus from the developments of technology in the intervening years – and these forces are growing, and will grow, stronger yet.

In the aircraft industry even a European approach cannot *guarantee* viability. In the year April 1965–April 1966 the U.S. aircraft industry sold approximately 400 civilian commercial aircraft throughout the world. The entire European industry sold less than 50. But a supra-national approach offers the only real *hope* of viability for non-American firms. And the approach needs to be *genuinely* supra-national. One of the problems about the Concord operation has been the duplication of production lines in the two countries, which with other complexities of cooperation has increased costs by about 25 per cent. We will need to do better than this if we are to compete effectively with the Americans.

A genuine European Technological Community, therefore, would need to embrace the following attributes:

(*a*) The establishment of genuinely *European* companies, through harmonization of company law and taxation, including legislation on patents, mergers and monopolies etc.

(*b*) Coordinating policies towards U.S. investment and the degree of protection to be accorded to Europe's science-based industries. Such policies should not be too protectionist. Britain and the Continent have much to gain from the inflow of U.S. capital and the import of U.S. know-how, both technological and managerial. We should not cut ourselves off from the benefits of U.S. expertise; equally, however, we should not allow ourselves to be swamped by it.

(*c*) Coordinating policies on public procurement, so that chosen firms can enjoy the benefits of really large-scale ordering.

(*d*) Development of supra-national manufacture on a planned basis in selected fields, such as aerospace, weapons systems, computers and nuclear power.

(*e*) Development of international specialization in R. & D. on a Continental basis, through development grants, encouraging the movement of scientists and technologists, and building up 'centres of excellence' to promote research in particular fields. Priority subjects for a European science policy might include, for example, research in oceanography, inter-urban transport systems, and micro-miniaturization in electronics; chemical engineering might be another field for specialization. Work might also be concentrated on developing atomic fast breeder reactors – where Britain has a clear technological lead – and communications satellites.

Behind all this is the underlying need to evolve, on a Continental basis, a strategy for technology which will determine the best allocation of scientific input – the task which, as we have seen, currently falls in our present national set-up to the Ministry of Technology. We have seen the complexities of this task on a purely national level. On a Continental level these complexities will of course be greatly magnified. Nevertheless, the task will have to be done at some stage if a European Technological Community is to become a reality.

Such a community must not, at the same time, be allowed to become an anti-American protectionist ring. Technological expertise can be bought at too high a price. To strike the balance which will make the best use of our resources, and enable us to develop our technologies without penalizing the domestic user, will call for immense skill – not to mention the political problems which will be involved in persuading the various European partners to accept the degree of discrimination which will be needed as between one European country and another in securing the most efficient allocation of work. A few years ago one would have said it was quite impossible. Now it merely looks heartbreakingly difficult.

## Can the New System Work?

In this chapter I have been discussing the work, pre-eminently, of two ministries – the D.E.A. and Technology. This has inevitably given a somewhat lopsided picture of the work of government in the field of growth planning and innovation. Other departments also of course have important roles to play – Housing, Defence, Education, the production ministries; one should not forget also the work of the Treasury in public sector management. Nevertheless, in some respects D.E.A. and Technology *do* differ from these established departments – in being new, without a major backlog of administrative and executive responsibilities, and in having an overriding commitment to *change*.

Before October 1964 there was one major government department dealing with the bulk of industry; now there are three. The Board of Trade and the Ministry of Technology both have sponsorship responsibilities for a wide range of industries, and functional responsibilities – Technology for R. & D., Trade for exports, commercial policy, competition and a number of other policies and services – covering the whole range of industry, sponsored and non-sponsored alike. The D.E.A., the focal point of industrial and economic policy, deals direct with industry through the E.D.C.s besides having responsibility for coordination of government policy on industry. This may be a dynamic structure, but it is also undeniably a clumsy one.

I believe the establishment of the D.E.A. and the Ministry of Technology has brought about – or at any rate accelerated – a radical change in the relationship between government and industry, which I believe to be right in present-day circumstances. There may now be a case for turning the Ministry of

Technology into a Ministry of Industry, by transferring to it – not necessarily all at once, but by degrees – the remaining sponsorship functions of the Board of Trade for specific industries. (This would still leave certain industries – building, food, energy, transport – under separate ministries, as they are now.) The Board of Trade would retain a large number of functional responsibilities, including responsibility for exports and commercial policy, and a wide range of services for industry. But Technology would become the focal point of contact between government and the bulk of industry – instead of, as today, about half of private industry.

In these circumstances there might well be a case for transferring some at least of the industrial advisers from the D.E.A. to the new Ministry of Industry. The Ministry of Industry would be the main voice of government in the E.D.C.s. It would still, however, be crucially important to retain an industrial voice in the central councils of the D.E.A., so that the link between industrial and economic growth policies remained strong.

It will be clear, I think, that I believe the reasoning which led to the establishment of the D.E.A. to be sound, and that it is vital to have at the centre of Whitehall a ministry whose concern is to see that the claims of long-term growth and efficiency are not swept aside, no matter what measures have to be taken to meet short-term crises or exigencies. Experience has not shown the differing viewpoints of the Treasury and D.E.A. to be irreconcilable in practice. Equally, however, it is too soon to say with conviction that the experiment has been a total success; and some administrative improvements plainly remain to be made if the new system is to function with maximum efficiency.

I have already mentioned one such improvement, in the possible simplification of industry–government relations by a transfer of functions from the Board of Trade – and to a lesser extent the D.E.A. – to a Ministry of Industry. But there are others which go, perhaps, rather deeper.

If government is to play the more active, interventionist, dynamic role *vis-à-vis* industry and the economy to which it now (in my opinion, rightly and inevitably) aspires, it needs to accept certain implications for the way in which it conducts its own affairs. In my experience, the Whitehall machine is often a very subtle and sensitive one for reacting to outside pressures and initiatives; it is not always as swift and effective in initiating action itself. This is partly because, unlike industry, government tends to operate at the policy-making level without clearly defined channels of command and executive responsibility, but through a proliferation of committees which represent the various interests involved. This is an excellent method of obtaining a consensus, but it does not always make for speed and decisiveness. As a dynamo, Whitehall can sometimes be depressingly sluggish. The desire for maximum consultation and consensus can too often lead to what might be called 'government by convoy' – that is, moving forward at the speed of the slowest (which can sometimes be very slow indeed).

If the decision-making machinery of government is to be made more effective, there might well be a case for an outside investigation – not into the content of policies, but into the mechanism for their formulation and implementation: an examination, in effect, of the committee and command structure in Whitehall. As we shall see in the next chapter, many leading business enterprises, both in the private and public sector, have in the last few years called in management consultants to examine their structure and to suggest improvements. These consultants do not normally question the objectives of the organizations they investigate. Their task is rather to see how these objectives can best be realized. Within the government service itself the use of consultants to advise on executive functions is growing. The Post Office, for example, in 1965 called in the American consultants McKinsey & Co., who had previously examined the management structure of companies like Shell, I.C.I., Dunlop and Vickers.

The business of government is, after all, in many ways like the business of running a large corporation – though it is normally more complex, and responds to somewhat different imperatives. Lessons of administration can be applied from one to the other. At a rather lower level, the existence of the Treasury's O. & M. (Organization and Methods) division, which has done much useful work in Whitehall, testifies to the importance of business efficiency in government.

I hope, therefore, that the Fulton Committee set up to look into the Civil Service at the beginning of 1966 will consider the possibility of an outside examination, in whole or in part, of the command and committee structure in Whitehall – purely from the viewpoint of administrative efficiency. I believe there may also be a case for establishing within the government machine a permanent internal business consultancy team, staffed initially by outside consultants and in the long term partly by civil servants who will have received special training in the team and partly by outside consultants on short-term secondment, to carry out a permanent probe into the methods and efficiency of Britain's biggest and most important business – the business of government.

It is arguable that the only effective way of streamlining government policy-making is to have a much smaller Cabinet, with ministries grouped under Cabinet ministries, through whom alone they can get access to the Cabinet – just as the three service ministers, for example, can now only get their views to Cabinet through the Secretary of State for Defence. It can be argued that so long as any one of twenty or more ministers can, if he wishes, take any issue to Cabinet, so long will there be pressure to compromise at official level right down the line, to avoid the escalation of policy differences between departments. In such circumstances 'government by convoy' may well be unavoidable.

There is, however, another factor which affects the ability of government to play a dynamic, innovatory role in the economy, quite apart from the internal efficiency and coherence of its organization. There is a deep-seated and entirely natural reluctance on the part of the average British civil servant to do anything which might expose his minister to *un mauvais quart d'heure* in the House of Commons at question-time. This means a reluctance to discriminate, to set a precedent, or to take risks with public money. Excellent as these inhibitions have been in the past, when government's role in the economy was primarily reactive and regulatory, they could be dangerous in an era of positive government. As M. Mendès-France used to say: '*Gouverner, c'est choisir.*' If government is to play a more positive role in energizing the economy and promoting innovation, it must be prepared to be less cautious and more discriminatory. Buggins must be denied his turn if need be. Inevitably in its new role government will incur the risk of making mistakes, and as one moves into an era of greater technological complexity this risk will grow. It can be reduced if government will equip itself with more business and specialist expertise, as it is starting to do. But it cannot be eliminated, and public opinion must be brought to recognize this and accept it as the price of progress.

Let it be clear that one is not here primarily criticizing the behaviour of civil servants. Civil servants exist to serve ministers. Ministers play the political game as best they can, and respond to the political pressures with which they are confronted. What one is criticizing is the impact of the parliamentary political game as at present played on the ability of government – any government – to play the kind of role it needs to play, and aspires to play, in promoting industrial efficiency within the confines of a mixed economy. The rules of the game can only be made more relevant to our present needs with the consent of public opinion. What one is asking is that a serious attempt be made to obtain that consent.

The changes in government policy and organization over the last few years have had profound effects upon the organization of both sides of industry. These effects are still working their way through the fabric of industry, and will continue to do so for some time. The first and most important effect has been to promote a major move towards centralization of authority. Both sides of industry have found that they need strong central organizations to represent them in the dialogue with government, whether in the Neddy organization or in some other forum. And, in order to negotiate with government, these central organizations have had to strengthen their hold over their own members. Thus, the T.U.C. is for the first time in its history scrutinizing the wage claims of its member unions to see that they conform to the prices and incomes policy, in an effort to avert tougher government measures. Such an assertion of T.U.C. authority over its members would have been almost unthinkable even a few years ago, whatever the motives which make it acceptable to trade unionists today.

But it is on the employers' side that the more radical changes have come. The need to present a united front – particularly in the Neddy Council – led the three leading employers' organizations (Federation of British Industries, British Employers Confederation, National Association of British Manufacturers) to seek a merger in 1964. The resulting body, the Confederation of British Industry (C.B.I.) is emerging as an extremely powerful, and on the whole progressive and constructive, spokesman for industry. Voluntary planning requires that the spokesmen for the three great interests – government, C.B.I. and T.U.C. – can establish a working partnership.

If this applies at national level, it is equally true at the level of the individual industry and firm. Industrial planning must rely heavily on the trade association as the main channel of communication with, and spokesman for, individual firms in a given industry. The ability of a Little Neddy, for example, to make effective contact with its industry depends to a considerable extent on the effectiveness and willingness to cooperate of the trade association network.

Unfortunately, many trade associations in Britain today

suffer from the same vices of excessive fragmentation and defensive-mindedness which characterize many of our trade unions. By and large, British industry suffers from too many trade associations, too high a proportion are still primarily concerned with some form or other of price maintenance, and too few do enough to help their members in improving efficiency.

It is inevitable that trade associations, like trade unions, will in a sense be conservative institutions. But there is a progressive form of conservatism which consists of intelligent reponse to current pressures and opportunities. The outlawing of resale price maintenance and other price agreements on the one hand, and the growth of planning – including the prices and incomes policy as well as Big Neddy and the Little Neddies – on the other, have created a whole new set of pressures and opportunities; and at the same time the C.B.I. has wisely tried to encourage a rationalization of trade associations and employers' organizations into bigger and more viable units wherever possible. This is a very important development, and it should lead to a more widespread transference of interest on the part of trade associations from price maintenance to providing services to improve their members' competitive ability. (Some particular examples of what is needed were given in the National Board for Prices and Incomes' first report, on the road haulage industry.)[15] This requires, of course, a readiness on the part of member-firms to give their associations the necessary financial support. We have tended in Britain to try to run both our trade unions and our trade associations on the cheap, and in neither case has it paid.

A modern-minded, forward-looking trade association with adequate resources can be an invaluable ally of a Little Neddy in initiating change which will benefit its industry; and in some cases this is indeed happening. But the benefit does not flow in one direction only. Planning gives the effective trade association a new power and importance *vis-à-vis* its members, as their spokesman to, and link with, the state. As we have seen, the more integrated and less compartmentalized a society, the more swiftly it is likely to be able to respond to technological change and to diffuse the benefits of such change. I therefore believe the current trend towards centralization could be desirable from the point of view of innovation as well as from the point of view of planning.

An effective prices and incomes policy, which will force both trade associations and unions away from concentration on their short-term sectional interests, is an important condition for this new approach. It follows that the antithesis which is sometimes made between inter-firm competition and Neddy-type planning is false. Only when firms cannot automatically pass cost increases on in higher prices will they turn whole-heartedly to meeting them by greater efficiency – which is what the Little Neddies are there to promote.

One other condition must be met if centralization is to promote change and innovation. It is that the *primum mobile* of the whole structure should itself be dedicated to change. Hence the importance of the D.E.A. and of a viable National Plan. Without these, there is of course a danger that the central authorities on each side might use their enhanced power and authority to enforce a rigid stability, resisting innovations which might upset the current balance of power and interests.

But the problem remains: how does one make the decisions of the Little Neddies meaningful to their constituents, where adequate channels of communication are lacking? This is of course not just a problem for the Little Neddies, but for the whole gamut of the D.E.A.'s operations: for the prices and incomes policy, the National Plan, and the regional policies as they emerge. All these are examples of planning by consent, and their ultimate sanction must be the force of public opinion. But how can consent be given or withheld if the detailed facts are not publicly known? There is a real danger of high-level bodies representing government, industry and the trade unions taking important decisions in committees *in vacuo* – to no effect, because in those places where real power resides, in the board-rooms and the factory floor, the message has not got through. If the Little Neddies are to do their job, there must be effective two-way communication between the high-powered committees in London and the grass-roots in industry up and down the country. The same applies, in hardly lesser degree, to the other aspects of the D.E.A.'s work. A certain amount can be done through existing bodies with a grass-roots organization like the British Productivity Council. But this in itself is not likely to be enough.

In my opinion a much greater effort at communication needs to be made, by government and Neddy, to overcome the dangers described above of a divorce between the planners in London and the decision-takers in industry itself. It is reasonable to hope that the C.B.I. and T.U.C., as co-sponsors of the Plan, will give their support to such an effort.

At the same time, direct and continuing contact needs to be opened up with the individual company and plant. Hitherto, as mentioned above, the dialogue has tended to be between government and trade association. But if government is to have the information it needs, and to be able to influence the thinking of individual companies directly, it has to establish direct lines of communication with at least the largest companies.

The importance, to industry and government, of a viable, credible National Plan has been stressed above. It is clear that the 1970 Plan was neither of these things, despite its many merits. In particular, it failed to distinguish sufficiently clearly between target and forecast, between prescription and predic-tion. This mistake must not be made in future plans.

A National Plan cannot of course follow exactly the pattern of individual corporate plans. For one thing, it has to cover a much wider time-span than the plans of individual companies. The meaningful time-horizon for planning varies greatly from firm to firm. In consumer goods manufacture it is rarely meaningful to look more than a few years ahead, and in this field most corporate plans take the form of firm predictions one or two years ahead, thereafter becoming increasingly vague (in contrast to the 1970 Plan, which gave a clear picture for a period five years hence, but said very little about the intervening years). In basic industry, on the other hand – energy, transport, steel, public infrastructure – the relevant planning period is very much longer. A National Plan has to try to say something meaningful to all types of industry.

The second difference is that the various elements in a National Plan are subject to widely varying degrees of government control, whereas in a corporate plan all elements are at least in theory subject to the control of the planners. In a National Plan the government has a substantial degree of control over those elements dependent on public expenditure, very much less over those in the private sector. Third, a National Plan – unlike corporate plans – has to be a published document, and regrettably it is almost impossible in our present political system for it not to become in some degree a political document.

However, when allowance has been made for these difficulties it nevertheless remains the case that the more closely the National Plan can be made to approximate to the best kinds of corporate plan, the more impact it is likely to make on business decisions. And, although British industry lags behind U.S. industry in this respect, corporate planning is acquiring greater respectability and greater sophistication in this country–helped by the circulation of such guides as Stanford's Long Range Planning Service. There is still too often a tendency to regard corporate planning as a separate function which can be hived off to the organization's economic department, rather than as something which must engage the attention of top management if it is to guide policy (and if it does not, it is virtually useless). But this is changing as management becomes more professionalized.

Greater coordination between the planning of government

and the larger individual enterprises should therefore benefit both. The dialogue between government and business, both on forecasting and on the more important question of policy-making, needs to be developed continuously in the years ahead, using whatever agencies and means are available, if the 'mixed economy' is to be dynamic and efficient. Both sides have a responsibility to see that this dialogue is frank, fruitful and unfettered by prejudice. For it is clear that no government in the years ahead is going to be able to disinterest itself in the performance of business, on which everything which government is pledged to achieve must ultimately depend. And this means that neither side can ever afford to ignore the other. They are condemned to partnership.

NOTES TO CHAPTER FIVE

1. See Preface (page 10).

2. I deal with this in more detail in my chapter, 'The Comforts of Stagnation', in the *Encounter* symposium *Suicide of a Nation?* (Hutchinson, 1963).

3. H.M.S.O., Cmnd 2764.

4. In its report on the printing industry (H.M.S.O., Cmnd 2750) in August 1965, the N.B.P.I. makes a point of recommending the Stationery Office to eliminate from its contracts with commercial printers any clause providing for variations in prices when wages vary. If, as a result, it found itself faced with higher initial prices in tenders, it should, says the N.B.P.I., refuse to concede them. This represents a conscious attempt to use public procurement to help break the automatic wage–price spiral in a particular industry.

5. But not for manufacturers, whose labour is actually made *cheaper* by S.E.T. This, on the face of it, highly retrograde step is justified on two counts: the need to secure a shift of labour in the long run out of the service trades into manufacturing (a dubious proposition), and the need to find some means of insulating our export industries from rising costs which does not contravene international agreements.

6. H.M.S.O., Cmnd 3167.

7. *Investment Appraisal* (H.M.S.O., 1965). In this section I have also drawn heavily on an article in the *Financial Times* of 29 January 1965 on 'What is the Worth of an Investment?' by Patrick Coldstream.

8. In this section 'engineering' refers predominantly to mechanical as opposed to electrical engineering, electronics or vehicles, but including machine tools.

9. The first three regional plans – for Central Scotland, North-east England and South-east England – were in fact all prepared and published by the Conservative government, and a number of others (including the Northern Ireland plan) were started under this government. The conversion to comprehensive regional planning had therefore gone a long way before the October 1964 election.

10. Perhaps one specific example will illustrate this. A few years ago, in my travels in Scotland, I came across a shipyard where the craft unions practised a strict limitation on intake of apprentices. Since there was a steady wastage of craftsmen to new industries in the locality, the number of permitted apprentices was declining – at a time when the shipyard had more orders than it could handle, and when there was a serious unemployed school-leaver problem in the area! This seemed a classic example of industrial suicide. Yet a few miles down the road, where a new electronics industry was operating, employing a substantial proportion of ex-shipyard labour, there appeared to be no demarcation problems or restrictive practices of any kind. Old industries can become prisoners of their pasts, from which new industries may if they are skilful remain immune.

11. H.M.S.O., Cmnd 2171.

12. In this section I draw heavily on an article, 'Research and Development in Electronic Capital Goods', by C. Freeman and others, in the *National Institute Economic Review*, November 1965.

13. H.M.S.O., Cmnd 2883.

14. H.M.S.O., Cmnd 2853.

15. H.M.S.O., Cmnd 2695.

# CHAPTER SIX

# THE MANAGEMENT OF INNOVATION

THIS book starts from the proposition that the rate of application of technology – the pace of innovation – lags in almost all cases behind the optimum, but that the lag is significantly greater in some countries, in some industries, in some firms than in others; and it seeks to identify some of the factors which enable some peoples and some enterprises to apply technology more successfully than others. I have argued that the climate of innovation is made up of a number of elements: the organization of government, social and cultural attitudes, standards and philosophies of education, and so on. In the last chapter I dealt at some length with the role that government can play. Nevertheless, as we saw at the end of the last chapter the positive contribution which government can make on its own is at best limited.

The pace of successful innovation depends in the last analysis on decisions taken in the boardrooms of private enterprise. Innovation is the function *par excellence* of the entrepreneur, of business management. If management, for one reason or another, cannot innovate fast enough or efficiently enough, no other element in society can fill the gap. Government can offer opportunities, smooth away obstacles, can do what it may to create the right kind of social climate, the right mixture of competition and expansion; but if the entrepreneurial mainspring is broken or weak, it will avail little.

In this chapter I propose to deal with what seem to me to be two of the main kinds of obstacles to successful innovation in industry. These are obstacles due to the calibre of management, and obstacles due to the nature and structure of the market. In the next chapter I will deal with the third, and in some ways the most complex, range of obstacles – those due to problems of manpower. The field covered by these two chapters is so vast that I fear the approach must inevitably be rather selective.

### 'What's Wrong With British Management?'

In the last few years books and articles with titles like this have been appearing on British bookstalls with almost sickening frequency, and the view has gained general currency that if anybody is to blame for our economic troubles, it is – more even than inefficient government or lazy workers – backward, amateur, slothful management. Naturally, like all exercises in mass indictment, this is a gross and unjust oversimplification. Many British managements are the equal of any in the world. Also, British industry has had to operate in an environment which is in many ways (some have been discussed above) less favourable to successful innovation than that of many of our competitors.

Nevertheless, there is an element of truth in the allegations that have been made – that the quality of large sectors of British management has in the post-war period been a bar to successful innovation: though I believe, as will be made clear below, that this is becoming less and less true as the decade wears on.[1]

In what follows I must confine myself to a limited, though vital, aspect of management performance. I am not concerned, for example, with assessing or explaining export performance, or industrial relations (though the latter will come into the next chapter). I am concerned solely with the quality of response to technology, with the pace of successful innovation.

It is plain that this is not just a question of inadequate investment. During the 1950s West Germany invested 21·3 per cent of her gross national product to achieve a growth rate of 7·4 per cent; France invested 17·6 per cent and grew at 4·6 per cent a year; the United Kingdom invested 14·5 per cent for a growth rate of 2·6 per annum. The variation in investment was much less than the variation in the return on investment. West Germany got almost twice the return on her investment that we did. And the return on investment is essentially a function of management. One reason for our relatively low return, it is clear, is that not enough of our investment was in sophisticated, labour-saving equipment – despite the fact that our labour force was growing more slowly than most of our competitors'. Part of the reason for this was given in the last chapter; part will be given in this; part in the next chapter.

At the beginning of the last chapter reference was made to the humanist bias in our educational system. To a remarkable degree the philosophy which informs British education, and the values to which it subscribes, pre-date the industrial revolution. One is reminded of the fact that our great public and grammar schools, and the ancient Oxbridge universities, grew up to serve an agrarian society, and that it is only in this century that the south of England, the centre of culture and political power, has become industrialized. In British society the successful entrepreneur has until recently been accorded a somewhat equivocal place – by comparison, for example, with the United States or Germany (or, today, Italy or France).

Consequently British industry, like other sectors of British life, has tended to be dominated by the cult of the amateur – the allegedly 'all-round' man, who is in fact typically a narrowly trained specialist in a non-technical subject. The proportion of senior management with technical qualifications has tended to be significantly lower in British industry than among most of our competitors. This reflects a combination of two factors – the comparatively low esteem in which business management has tended to be held in the past by the nation's academic elite (which accounts for the comparatively small proportion of university graduates in industry), and the preference shown in industry as in other sectors for the 'arts' man over the technologist.

Fortunately for Britain, both these trends are now much less in evidence than they were. A survey by the Institute of

Directors a few years ago showed that of the general managers of large firms in Britain over the age of sixty, only 11 per cent were university graduates. For those under forty, the proportion was 30 per cent. More recent surveys have confirmed this trend. Nevertheless, too much of the tone of business is still set by the 'old guard', and this undoubtedly retards progress.

Defenders of the traditional system normally advance two main arguments. First, they argue that the 'specialist' (which normally means the technical man) has an insufficiently commercial approach and a narrow view of the managerial function. In so far as this is true (and there is some evidence that it has been in the past), it is a criticism of the way we train our technologists in this country. The experience of other countries shows that there is no reason why the engineer or scientist should lack commercial acumen; indeed, his expertise should make him a better salesman. But it does seem that exports of British heavy industry products have sometimes suffered in recent years through being entrusted to engineers with inadequate ability in finance and marketing matters.

This is a reflection of the excessive specialization which, in my view, has been one of the major defects of British education. The *genuine* 'all-round' man should have a knowledge of the sciences as well as the arts; he should be numerate as well as literate. The inability of the technical man and the arts man to communicate effectively with each other reflects the 'compartmentalization' which, as I have suggested above, is one of the major causes of our slow application of technology (and which, as we have seen, also troubles American industry).

The second traditional argument is that the expert should be 'on tap and not on top' – that his function should be to advise but not to take decisions (for fear, presumably, that his specialist expertise might warp his judgement). It is true, of course, that a board of directors all of whom were, shall we say, expert nuclear physicists, might take some odd decisions – though not necessarily odder than a board consisting entirely of, say, historians or lawyers. But the correct answer to this is that a board should contain a proper balance of specialisms – not that all specialists should be excluded from it. (In any event, some specialists in British industry are more equal than others; accountants, as a group, have established themselves firmly in the boardroom – too firmly, it might be argued.)

The idea of the expert sitting in the proverbial back room to answer questions from his executives is somewhat naïve. As technology advances, the situation is increasingly being reached in which non-technical boards do not know what questions to ask their specialists, and do not understand the answers when they get them. As we saw in Chapter 2, this is hardly a satisfactory situation; and it will get worse as technology becomes more complex. There is no solution, other than to get more technologists into decision-making posts, and to do whatever can be done to break down the barriers between the cultures.

One of the great weaknesses of the traditional type of business management is its inability to absorb skills and techniques which it does not itself possess. Since the war there has been a rapidly growing trend towards the recruitment of graduates in industry. At the same time, industry has significantly enhanced its position in the 'pecking-order' for graduates choosing jobs. Its status has greatly improved. This is, I am convinced, a trend of enormous long-term importance and value. It means that, as the intellectual content of the managerial function increases, so the intellectual calibre of British management should go up too. I believe that, partly because of the higher intellectual level of the recent intake and partly for other reasons which will be given below, managerial standards are on an upward trend in this country, and this is one of the factors providing grounds for hope in our economic future.

At the same time the absorption of graduates into industry has been by no means painless. Many graduates have found themselves frustrated because their firms were not really geared to make use of their talents. Even today, though matters are considerably improved, the graduate intake is still concentrated in a relatively small band of businesses; there is still a depressingly large number of concerns which would literally not know what to do with a graduate if they got one (unless he was the boss's son!). This situation is, of course, by no means confined to this country; but that is no reason for being complacent about it.

But the problems of absorption appear to be significantly greater for the technical or science graduate who wants to practise his specialism than they are for the arts graduate who enters the general-management stream. A few years ago there was considerable, and justified, concern about the rate at which we were turning out highly qualified scientists and technologists. In the last few years there has been a substantial expansion in higher technical education, and the problem has ceased to be one of supply and instead become one of demand. We seem to be in some danger of over-supply of technological graduates – not because we are in fact producing too many, but because the effective absorption rate in industry is still too low. Hence the phenomenon of the 'brain drain'. It has not been widely enough recognized that this 'drain' is a phenomenon which affects almost all underdeveloped countries. These countries start by giving their best young people education in the skills which their country is going to need if it is to develop. But in too many cases these people complete their education before their country is in fact in a position to use their talents adequately. So they go where their talents *are* rewarded – that is, to the more developed countries, who have least need of them but who are best equipped to absorb them. Thus the West African engineer or doctor tends to come to Britain, and the British space technologist to go to America. The 'brain drain' is a reflection of the technical backwardness of the drained country.

It is not true that British 'brains' are lured to the United States simply by higher salaries. They go, partly for better material conditions, partly to gain more experience, partly because they feel that they will have more interesting and congenial work and more appreciation and status. How serious this is depends on the degree of permanency of their stay. If they go to the United States for a few years and then return to this country, having absorbed the lessons of their American experience, this country will be the beneficiary. But if they stay in the United States for the bulk of their working life, the money invested by Britain in their education will of course have been wasted. But the answer rests primarily with British management (and to a much smaller extent with government). It is up to them to create the kind of organizations which can usefully absorb the growing output of trained technologists, and provide them with the opportunities to which they – not unreasonably – feel entitled.

It is often argued, with I believe some element of truth, that high levels of marginal personal taxation in this country make it impossible for British employers to offer attractive rates of take-home pay for American-trained British executives and technologists. It is certainly true that a disturbingly large proportion of British graduates of the Harvard Business School, for example, tend to take up employment with North American rather than British firms. But tax is I believe only part of the reason for the undoubted salary discrepancies. Another complicating factor is the excessive rigidity of the managerial salary scales in the typical large British firm. These inhibit the average British employer from offering the right rate for the exceptional high-flyer, because to offer the market rate would mean upsetting the traditional differentials with more senior management – who because of high surtax rates may have no incentive to raise their *own* salaries – and would also put the high-flyer in an apparently unduly favoured position *vis-à-vis* other younger managers. Too often British employers appear unready to upset traditional management salary structures in order to accommodate the brilliant younger man, or the one with special expertise. This may be due to an undue deference to tradition, or to an undervaluation of the kinds of expertise taught in business schools or similar institutions, or both. In any case the result is highly unsatisfactory. American firms, less inhibited about salary differentials, more ready to buy skills at the market price (and in some cases at least with a shrewder idea what that price is), are acquiring too large a proportion of our best-trained young managers and technologists; and Britain is in danger of acquiring a reputation as a country inhospitable to excellence. The real criticism that can be made of our tax structure in this respect is that it contributes to this state of affairs, and that it provides an obvious alibi for managers unwilling to expose themselves to too close contact with colleagues who might reveal their deficiencies or impose unwelcome changes. It is thus one more factor inclining Britain towards stagnation rather than dynamism. But it is not the only factor, nor in my opinion the most important.

Allied to the question of absorbing scientific talent is that of absorbing scientific information. This is a problem of rapidly growing complexity. It has been calculated that of all the scientists who have ever lived, seven eighths are alive and working today. In the last decade and a half the number of scientific periodicals throughout the world has increased by over 40 per cent. There are now estimated to be over 80,000 regular scientific journals and more than 1,500 abstract journals in the world. Vastly more information than ever before is being generated, of vastly greater complexity; vastly more is being sought, at ever greater speed. It has been argued, only half-jocularly, that under present conditions in almost all cases it is quicker to undertake one's own research into a problem than to find out whether somebody else has already solved it for one. Hence the growing importance of the information scientist, and of improving techniques of information retrieval.

The Russians estimate that, in order to reduce the incidence of 'reinvention', of duplication of research, it may be necessary to concentrate as much as one fifth of national scientific effort on providing scientists with libraries. The problem is now beginning to be tackled at national level in this country, by the establishment of a Government Office of Scientific and Technical Information, and the organization by the National Electronics Research Council of a computer-controlled lending library for research workers in radio and electronics. In this field, not surprisingly, we lag behind the Americans with their huge information retrieval projects, at N.A.S.A., Institute of Applied Technology, the M.I.T. information project, and so on. In all cases techniques for coding information need to be further refined. The ultimate aim must be devices which can read, index and store millions of complete documents, in such a way that their contents can be rapidly recovered by a means capable of expressing concepts rather than rigid subject parameters.

The computer, with its memory store, is of course an ideal instrument for this; indeed, without computers this kind of project would be impossible. The development of the computer as an information store is of course going to affect radically the conduct of business operations. As we saw in Chapter 4, it is going to make it much easier for management to concentrate on the really critical decisions, with the more routine operations currently performed by junior or middle management increasingly left to the computer, to feed instructions out from its memory. It is an essential task of modern management to see that the necessary information for the future technical advance of the organization is being properly communicated, organized and stored, and that the amount of re-invention and research duplication is reduced to a minimum.

## The Cult of the Professional

Within the last few years the cult of the amateur in British business management has begun to give way to something like an opposing cult of the professional. This has been largely an inevitable response to an increasingly competitive and an increasingly technology-dominated environment. But it has been helped forward by at least three major developments, which I propose to examine briefly in turn. These are:

(1) The rapid growth in management consultancy and similar services, stimulated by invasion from the United States;

(2) A much accelerated pace of management mobility, helped forward by the development of the management selection consultants;

(3) The boom in business education.

The role of consultants has been looked at in the American context in Chapter 2. Their role in innovation is essentially threefold. First, they act as transmitters of ideas and techniques from one branch of industry to another. Second, they help to raise standards in those firms they advise. Third, by applying a critical independent eye to a concern's operations, they help management itself to become more self-critical.

Management consultancy in Britain has a long and distinguished history, but British management consultants have never acquired the status and prestige of their American counterparts. They have tended historically to be used to solve problems of factory-floor organization rather than the higher-level problems of business strategy and company organization and structure. Too much of their work has been on the shop-floor – method study schemes, factory layout, and so on: too little in the boardroom. This has not really been their fault; it has been the fault of the environment in which they have had to operate. The traditional attitude of British management has been that it is indecent for outsiders to expect to pry into its affairs, and that to call in a consultant is an admission of failure, a sign that one doesn't know how to run one's business. Management has been felt to be an incommunicable art, only to be learned by practice and application. How, then, can an outsider, however brilliant, be expected to teach one anything useful about the job to which one has devoted a lifetime?

The American business environment, as we have seen, has been very different – much more professional, much less secretive, much more open to objective evaluation and measurement of performance. In this climate consultancy has flourished.

It has also, as we have seen, become an increasingly competitive, in some ways overcrowded, profession. At the end of the fifties, in consequence, a large-scale expansion of U.S. consultant and contract research services began in Europe and the United Kingdom, where the market was far less developed and where there was a growing desire to absorb American techniques and 'know-how'. The movement was well timed. Not all the new arrivals were successful. Some consultants who were, and are, highly regarded in the United States have failed to make an impression on this side of the Atlantic. But some have been notably successful.

In the United Kingdom, to date, the two that have probably made most impact have been McKinsey and Emerson, both of whom have provided specialized services which British consultants had tended hitherto to ignore. Emerson's expertise has been, as we saw in Chapter 1,[2] in labour utilization schemes. McKinsey has concentrated, by contrast, on schemes for the reorganization of company structures and chains of command – work which involves operating at boardroom level. In the space of a few years it has become, from a mark of shame, almost a status symbol to employ a consultant like McKinsey, and most of the best companies in the land now go out of their way to announce that they are working with consultants. This is perhaps the most remarkable sign of the change in boardroom climates in British industry in the last few years – the tangible evidence of the triumph of the professional over the amateur.

Contract research firms have shared in this boom. Arthur D. Little, for example, has been employed on diversification plans for Short aircraft works in Belfast, and – with the British A.I.C.

– on detailed Anglo-American productivity comparisons in selected industries for the U.K. government. McKinsey, having investigated a substantial proportion of the biggest private companies in Britain, was invited at the beginning of 1965 to recommend improvements in the structure and organization of the Post Office – a significant move into the formerly restricted field of government. Stanford has done much work on the Continent, rather less as yet in the United Kingdom.

There has been some resentment among British consultants at the proportion of 'plum' jobs going to the Americans, and it still seems to be true that a British company finds it more prestigious to hire an American than a British consultant. There is without doubt an element of fashion in this. Nevertheless, the evidence suggests that American parentage is not a sufficient condition for approval among the fashion setters in British industry. Not every American consultant operating in the U.K. has enjoyed anything like the success achieved by McKinsey. Second, there is a not unjustified feeling that in employing an American consultant one is gaining access to a much wider experience from a more technologically advanced country than one could get from a British consultant. What the U.S. consultant has to offer is the transference of American experience and 'know-how' to British conditions – and such transference, while risky if badly handled, can be uniquely valuable if the transplantation is done skilfully. In the same way British consultants have developed flourishing practices in many overseas countries who are anxious to absorb British experience and 'know-how' – including the United States itself. I believe that the international exchange of expertise through consultancy services is a valuable trend which is bound to grow. Also, there is a growing trend for U.S. and British consultants to pool their expertise on major contracts by forming consortia or subcontracting work to each other.

In any event, galling as it may be to British pride to seem to follow in the wake of foreign incomers, the fact is that a great part of the boom in management consultancy – particularly at the higher levels of business decision – has spilled over into the British firms. Though the Americans may make the headlines, by far the largest proportion of consultancy work in Britain today is being done by British consultants, and the rate of expansion – both quantitatively and in terms of the range and complexity of assignments – is very great. Indeed, the profession is working at full stretch, with little if any available spare capacity, with demand rising at an average 15 per cent a year. Consultancy has plainly 'arrived' (as was shown by the appointment in 1964 of the chairman of the Management Consultants Association to a seat on the Neddy Council among the princes of British industry).

It is important to get a proper sense of the scale of operation of the various consultant organizations. McKinsey's U.K. organization, for example, contains some 50 or so consultants (about 75 per cent British). Each of the Big Four British consultants (Urwick Orr, A.I.C., Production-Engineering, P.A. Management Consultants) has more than 300. Although for professional reasons British consultant firms are more inhibited than Americans about advertising their successes, in fact one or more of them works or has worked in recent years in almost all the larger British manufacturing concerns.

But it is not only from the Americans that competition is growing for the traditional 'multi-purpose' management consultants. Indeed, the position in Britain today is very similar to the situation at the end of the fifties in the United States described in Chapter 2. On both sides of the Atlantic the major accounting firms have been developing large management consulting divisions. Six of the leading British ones – Cooper Brothers, Annan Impey Morrish, Binder Hamlyn & Fry, Peat Marwick Mitchell, Price Waterhouse and Robson Morrow – have now joined the Management Consultants Association along with the Big Four. The merchant banks are also showing growing interest in this field.

Again, as the traditional gulf between academic and business life in Britain narrows, the practice of professors in business schools and elsewhere supplementing their income by consulting is on the increase, as in the United States.

The management selection and executive search business, which has made great strides in the United Kingdom in recent years, is also closely linked with management consultancy. Some of the Big Four operate their own management selection sections. Also related to management consultancy is the work of the engineering consultants, a field where the British have long enjoyed an international reputation.

More recently there has been a great expansion in another kind of specialized professional consultancy, closely linked to management. These are the so-called 'management science' consultants, specialists in operational research and other quantitative computer-based techniques, such as Metra-Sigma-Martech and Business Operations Research. The former is a particularly interesting development. It has had an exceptionally rapid growth in the last few years. It is one of the very few genuinely 'European' consultants, being a member of Metra International which brings together management research firms of six European countries. Metra-Sigma aims to cover economic and social development, management organization, communications and control, marketing, national and urban planning, systems analysis and design, corporate and product planning and many other fields where, as it says, 'an analytical approach to problems can promote growth and profitability'. It has a professional staff of over 400, one of the largest data processing installations in Europe, and a very wide range of clients in governments, nationalized and private industries on both sides of the Atlantic. In the United Kingdom Sigma (the letters stand for 'Science in General Management') is linked with a market research organization, Martech, and a product-planning subsidiary, Proplan. It represents therefore an exceptionally widely based integrated service hinged on the application of computer-based O.R. and systems analysis.

There are other more specialized consultant firms which have carved out a particular niche for themselves, such as E. G. Brisch in stock analysis and classification. And, as in the United States, client firms have themselves increasingly begun to set up their own 'management services' departments to undertake internal consultancy work.

Another specialist approach leading increasingly into general management problems has been by way of economic analysis. An outstandingly successful British example of this has been the Economist Intelligence Unit (an offshoot of the *Economist*), which competes in many fields with organizations like Stanford and Arthur D. Little.

So the British consultancy picture resembles that which we saw in the United States in Chapter 2, with a growing pro-liferation of all types of consultants: some 'generalists' like the Big Four in Britain or McKinsey, Booz Allen and so on in the United States, some specialists, some organizations moving into general management problems from specialist bases – contract research as with A.D.L., operational research as with Sigma, economic research as with the Economist Intelligence Unit, accounting, management selection, etc. To complete the picture one should mention the tendency of some of the Big Four them-selves to seek links with some of the specialists, particularly in the computer field. Thus Urwick Orr has formed a partnership with the U.S. computer specialist John Diebold. A.I.C. has set up its own management sciences subsidiary.

Thus, as we saw in the United States in Chapter 2, current British experience in consultancy demonstrates the need for a multi-discipline approach to industrial problems (including those of governments) and the impossibility of confining problem-solving within the confines of rigid parameters of subject and technique. Another trend of growing importance is the internationalization of consultancy work. Most of the main consultant firms have an international clientele. And I believe it will not be long before the genuinely 'European' or even 'Atlantic' consultant organization is the norm. Metra-Sigma-Martech provides one example. Other consultant firms are trying to internationalize their organizations or to build up close links with consultants in other countries. The analogy with the multi-disciplinary approach is exact. Increasingly business is operating on an international scale, and having to face the problems of international operation. Increasingly, too, there is realization of the extent to which answers to particular problems may be found by studying the lessons of other countries. The day of the purely national large-scale consultant is, I believe, almost over; at least on this side of the Atlantic.

One aspect of the consultancy boom has been the growing interest in business techniques, most of which either originated or have been developed in the United States. British use of these techniques has become increasingly widespread and sophisticated, and in some cases – e.g. operational research and network analysis – we are as advanced as any country in the world, including the United States. These techniques are part of the tool-bag of consultancy, though a good consultant will never try to employ a particular technique as a panacea for all problems. We have already looked at three of the most important in the current range of techniques – operational research, network analysis and the D.C.F. method of investment appraisal. Other techniques deal with such matters as incentive payments schemes (like the Rucker Plan employed by Emerson at the former Pressed Steel plant at Linwood in Scotland), methods of staff appraisal, personnel recruitment, salary planning and management development; these are all ways of making the best use of one's personnel by scientific methods. Another field for the application of new techniques is training. 'Programmed learning', with scientifically programmed teaching machines, enables factual instruction to be given more swiftly and often more efficiently than through live, human teachers.

Programmed learning could have an importance beyond the industrial field, if the nation is to meet its education targets in the years ahead despite the teacher shortage.

Psychological techniques are increasingly being used to guide recruitment and promotion policies, to assess staff and management capabilities, and to probe human relations problems. The widening use of group dynamics techniques is significant in this field. Of equal significance in the training and executive development field is the growing use of Business Games, simulating actual management situations; these may well play an increasing part in the curricula of the new business schools and staff colleges.

Another technique of growing importance in the United Kingdom today is Value Analysis (or Value Engineering). Unlike most of the new techniques, it is a psychological discipline rather than a statistical tool; the approach is qualitative rather than quantitative. Where network analysis, for example, studies a process, value analysis examines the product. It seeks to study the *function* of the product – whether it be a submarine or a screw-thread – to see whether this function can be equally or better performed in cheaper ways. It conducts a kind of striptease operation on the product, to try to find out which aspects confer value on it, and whether costs can be reduced by eliminating the others. In a sense this is no more than conventional 'cost reduction' scientifically applied. But the type of approach and the mental disciplines involved do seem to represent a significant advance.

None of these new techniques is a 'cure-all' – and none of them, and no consultant, can do management's job for it. Some of the techniques – particularly the psychological ones – can be positively dangerous unless handled with wisdom and commonsense. But collectively they do add up to a formidable armoury of weapons for discriminating, professional management to use.

There are also many business techniques of a lower standard of complexity and sophistication which are yet of crucial

T – T.I. – I.

importance to industrial efficiency. The last chapter showed the scope in Britain today for greater Variety Control, for example. Again, Work Study or Work Measurement is a well-established practice of many years' standing; but its degree of acceptance still varies significantly from firm to firm, and from industry to industry. The Geddes Report on the British shipbuilding industry[3] pointed out the importance of a wider use of simple work measurement techniques in meeting the problems of the British shipyards in 1966.

Important also for general efficiency are the various techniques of control designed to keep the different functions of the enterprise in balance – production control, stock control, quality control, budgetary control; and the accompanying techniques of improved plan layout and materials handling. These techniques are applicable to large and small firms alike, and are an integral part of corporate planning, or – as it is now widely and attractively called – Planning by Objective. It is an illusion to think that the skills and techniques of the consultant or efficiency expert are applicable only to the giant firm or the 'whiz-kids' of industry – as dangerous an illusion as the earlier one that they were only for pale-eyed dreamers, and not for hard-headed practical men.[4]

Allied to the management consultants are the management selection firms who help to solve industry's problems of executive recruitment for it (and, on occasion, help to find new jobs for executives who wish, or are forced, to leave their existing firms). The growing importance of this type of activity can be gauged by a glance through the advertisement columns of the posher Sunday papers almost any week in the year. Its value in raising the standards of British management and in spreading new ideas and new techniques is equally great.

In contrast to America, British business management has traditionally been very immobile. A large proportion of executives have spent their entire working life virtually with a single firm, whether they entered it as a management trainee or worked their way up from the shop floor. This has had a number of bad effects. Some companies have suffered from acute shortages of management talent; this has not unnaturally been a particularly serious headache for expanding businesses. Moreover, the tendency to recruit executives by internal promotion has encouraged conservatism, an inbred approach and a lack of awareness of what is going on elsewhere. It has slowed down the diffusion of new methods and ideas; and in some of the older, more traditionally minded industries the effect has been almost suffocating.

Today all this is changing. Managerial mobility has been greatly increased, and an active market in executives has developed. As a result expanding companies have had a major bottleneck removed, and new ideas are travelling through the economy with increasing rapidity. The techniques of one industry are being applied to others, with considerable success. The footloose professional manager, bringing enlightenment to backward areas of the economy – personified by Dr Beeching – is beginning to become almost as common a feature of the British scene as of the American. (At the same time, of course, the backward industries are finding their privacy increasingly violated by competition from the newer technologies – as the natural textile fibres by I.C.I. and Courtaulds – and the takeover bid is similarly forcing backward management into liquidation.)

All this is highly desirable. It is being helped forward by a third major trend, the rapid growth in business education. As we have seen, until recently Britain and other European countries lagged far behind the United States in the scope and range of business education. Today the United Kingdom would appear to have moved ahead of all other European countries in this field.

The reasons for the lag are not far to seek. As we have seen, the attitude of the educational authorities here has traditionally been far more negative than in the United States, and the prevailing academic view was that management had no intellectual content worthy of the name. This was also the view of the bulk of British industry, which argued that management could only be taught 'on the job'.

However, during the forties and fifties a steady growth of management training courses took place: partly in independent institutions like the pioneer Administrative Staff College at Henley and Ashridge College; partly in summer schools and staff colleges run by individual industries and companies, and by some of the management consultant firms (the British, not the American); partly by a number of technical colleges, colleges of advanced technology and provincial universities who taught the Diploma of Management Studies. The trouble with this effort was that it was too diffused – most of the organizations teaching business studies were below the threshold of efficient size – and it lacked prestige. Industry felt that something better was needed, and (with exceptions) tended not to patronize what was already available, with the result that standards sank.

By 1963 it was clear that something further would need to be done. There was a growing demand in industry for more and better facilities for business education on the American model. Academic opinion was coming rapidly round to the need for teaching at a higher level than the Diploma studies could provide. The trouble was that the businessmen and the academics could not agree on either the content or the organization of the courses both agreed were necessary. Fortunately both agreed to refer the matter to an outside arbitrator, Lord Franks. The Franks Report, in November 1963, recommended the establishment in the first instance of two full-time graduate business schools, roughly on the Harvard model, at London and Manchester universities. The constitution was sensibly devised to ensure due representation of business and academic interests, and the content of the courses to be taught was, equally sensibly, left to the discretion of the future directors. It was envisaged that each school should provide both a Master's degree course for immediate postgraduates and post-experience courses for more senior men who had had some years in industry.

The two business schools are now in operation, and it is clear that other universities will follow with full-scale graduate business schools before long. An increasing number of universities – including, for example, Oxford, Warwick, Birmingham, Bradford, Liverpool and Glasgow – are offering some form or other of business study courses. The institutions previously in the field are themselves in most cases attracting a bigger demand for their services than in the past. The Harvard Business School has run extremely successful advanced summer schools in this country for senior British businessmen, as well as helping to train British business teachers. Ashridge has recently been rejuvenated, and now runs a wide range of specialized courses highly effectively. The College of Aeronautics at Cranfield has diversified into management studies, with courses more closely based on Harvard techniques than are available elsewhere in Britain.

This is highly encouraging. But the priorities for the next phase of business education need to be thought out carefully. It is desirable that there should be a number of graduate business schools, each developing its own philosophy of education so that the ideal content for studies and the ideal method of teaching can be evolved through trial and error. It is desirable, too, that three separate main needs should be catered for. The general postgraduate course – which will provide a common set of ideas and a *lingua franca* for tomorrow's professional managers and technocrats – and the advanced post-experience course, for men moving from specialist functions into general management, can be provided by the business schools (and, in the latter case, by Henley). More specialized courses in particular management functions (production, marketing, personnel, finance, etc.), and techniques, and for the special needs of particular industries, can best be catered for by the C.A.T.s and technical colleges, the management consultants and others. So far there would seem to be general agreement.

But this still leaves some serious gaps, and a problem of quality and resources. The gaps are at both ends of the scale. At the top, there is a serious problem for the senior manager, who cannot or will not 'go back to school' himself, but who needs to know at least enough about the new methods not to frustrate or thwart the efforts of the more junior men in his firm who *have* been through the courses. The incomprehension of senior management has in more than one case destroyed much of the benefit which younger men have derived from attending business courses, because it has prevented them from applying in their own firms the lessons they have learned. The success of the Harvard summer schools has shown the demand that exists here. What seems to be required is an intensive campaign of 'in-firm' executive development courses at the highest level. This will be hard to organize, and expensive in manpower. But without it much of the immediate benefit from the spread of business education will be lost.

Second, there is a danger in assuming that the only executive worth educating is the graduate. A great deal more needs to be done at a rather lower level, to educate the non-graduate who will for a very long time to come provide the bulk of British management, and who needs an understanding of the new techniques as much as his more intellectual colleague; and, in particular, more needs to be done for the executive in the small firm, who cannot spare the time or the money to attend a full-time post-degree course. The business schools should be seen as one element in a comprehensive scheme for business education – not as the whole solution to the problem.

At the same time, there is a strong case for trying to achieve a greater concentration of resources, so as to raise the general standard of business teaching. The British Institute of Management does provide some guidance as to the content and standards of different courses on offer; without this guidance the choice of an appropriate course on which to send an executive can be a very difficult one for a firm to make. But it would probably be desirable to have some certification system for all courses, as a test of quality standards; and the whole field of management education and development could probably benefit from some kind of central policy direction.

This is particularly difficult because of the number of different organizations involved – not least in Whitehall. Responsibility for the *supply* of suitable management courses rests with the Department of Education and Science. Responsibility for *demand* is more fragmented. The D.E.A. is concerned through its overall responsibility for economic growth and industrial efficiency. The Board of Trade is concerned as the sponsor department for the B.I.M. and the British Productivity Council. The Ministry of Labour is involved in its capacity as parent to the Central Training Council and the various industrial training boards, which include management training among their interests. The Ministry of Technology is concerned with increasing technological awareness among managers. Outside government and the educational and professional organizations, the C.B.I. as the voice of industry has a major interest. In order to avoid waste of scarce resources and to bring demand and supply into closer alignment – qualitatively as well as quantitatively – there would seem to be an urgent need for some kind of central co-ordinating machinery, bringing together the governmental, industrial and educational interests involved.

At all events, the leaven of professionalism is now clearly working through British industry, with beneficial results. An increasing number of companies are now operating sophisticated programmes of forward corporate planning on the American model, with control systems which are increasingly computer-based. In the larger companies at least, British management is beginning increasingly to respond to the opportunities offered by technology.

## The Large and the Small

The trouble is, however, that a large proportion of British industry consists of small firms; and, while there is no necessary relationship between size and efficiency, many of the trends of modern technology do appear to favour large units. Large firms can more readily afford to use management study courses, to employ consultants and to have R. & D. departments than small firms. Even more important, the hardware required for successful innovation costs money, which may be beyond the resources of a small firm. Computers are not cheap items of equipment, nor is the capital machinery required to set up automated production lines.

There is therefore a growing danger of the emergence of a kind of 'dual economy' in British industry, just as exists in Japan and in countries like France and Italy; on the one hand a highly advanced sector of mainly large firms, employing all types of modern technology (both hardware and software); on the other a wide fringe of mainly small firms, operating at a lower level of sophistication, unable to profit from the discoveries of technology, depressing the level of the whole economy. The picture is of course oversimplified, but something like this does seem to be happening in most industrial countries.

So far the operation of the governmental planning techniques described in the last chapter has, indeed, tended to widen this gulf, as it has in other countries practising indicative planning. It is the large companies and not the small which tend to be represented on the Little Neddies and other bodies set up to advise Whitehall. It is the large companies who can afford to second top people to work in government as industrial advisers, to sit on committees of inquiry, and so on. It is the large companies whose performance and prospects are scanned earnestly by the planners, and whose views tend to get fed into the government machine through one channel or another. The government–industry dialogue is essentially a dialogue between government and *large* industry – and this is perhaps inevitable. (Indeed, I suggested in the last chapter that the dialogue needs to be intensified.) But we should never allow ourselves to forget that the bulk of British industry consists of small firms, many of whom inhabit a very different world and respond to very different stimuli from the giants with whom Whitehall normally converses.

I think it would be helpful if this were more explicitly recognized than it has been hitherto in the next stage of growth planning by government. One has to start somewhere, and it made sense to start by concentrating on the large firms. But I believe there is a case for some form of Small Business Administration in the United Kingdom, as there is in the United States, which could help small firms specifically through such measures as state-aided consultancy services, dissemination of technical knowledge, and others. A start has indeed already been made with the Industrial Liaison Service of the Ministry of Technology and the Small Business Centre attached to the University of Aston in Birmingham, and one would hope that these local and sectoral approaches will develop and receive reinforcement at national level as time goes on. The National Agricultural Advisory Service shows what can be done in a specific sector.

There are of course a large number of organizations, both public and private, which provide management services of one kind or another and with different degrees of sophistication, suitable for smaller firms. There is the British Productivity Council with its local associations. There is the Centre for Interfirm Comparisons, the British Institute of Management, the professional and trade associations (some a good deal more useful than others in this area), the advisory services established by the Production Engineering Research Association (P.E.R.A.) and one or two others. One of the most sensible decisions of the first National Productivity Conference in the autumn of 1966 was to initiate a comparative study of the various organizations involved, to try to assess relative cost/benefit performances, and to determine the scope for rationalization and coordination and the main areas still unexploited.

Perhaps more important, however, than the size of the firm is the size and structure of the market it is supplying. Automation in the sense we are considering it in this book represents, after all, simply an extension of the process of substituting capital for labour which has been going on since the industrial revolution – but it is a big leap forward along the path. Substituting capital for labour involves raising the fixed overhead costs and reducing the variable costs. It follows that the break-even point at which the plant can operate is raised, to cover the overheads; but the marginal cost of extra output is correspondingly much lower. The more capitalized a plant, therefore, the larger the market it needs, and the more standardized; for the fixed capital equipment can only earn its keep if it can operate on reasonably long production runs. One cannot, therefore, operate a highly-capitalized plant profitably on a jobbing basis. Automation requires, if it is to pay off, long runs of fairly standardized products; it cannot succeed if the customer insists on undue variety or on placing his orders in small lots. This applies to almost any continuous process industry, be it steel, aluminium, paper or chemicals. If one has to keep stopping the production lines in order to change the product, the costs mount rapidly. (We saw in Chapter 5 the importance of greater variety control in raising the performance of British industry generally.) Too much of British industry still operates on what is essentially a jobbing basis, instead of applying a dynamic marketing policy.

Take for example the printing industry. Printing today represents one of the great survivals of craft industry in a technological age. Many of its basic processes have changed remarkably little since the days of Caxton. It is an industry which still operates largely on a jobbing basis, and is still in the main dominated by small (often family) firms. But there is perhaps no other major industry today to which the application of electronic processes presents greater opportunities for technical advance – perhaps the greatest for printing since the invention of movable type.

The job of the compositor can be almost completely eliminated by computer or film-type setting. Type-setting work can be cut from a matter of months to a matter of hours –though before the computer can process the tape it still has to be produced at human speeds. The film-setter is not in fact a particularly new invention; it was first patented by Friese-Green in the 1890s. But on both sides of the Atlantic its practical application has been slow. The first computer-typesetting concerns in Europe became operational only three or four years ago. The first newspaper to use computer typesetting and other automated processes in this country, Lord Thomson's Reading *Evening Post*, was launched in September 1965.

Innovation is not likely to stop there. Simply by applying inventions already developed over the last half-century the entire technology and structure of printing can be transformed. The newspaper of the future will record all editorial matter on a computer 'memory', and no type need be set until a minute or so before printing. The words will go on to film, instead of being cast in metal as now, and simultaneous printing can take place in different cities at the press of a button. The job of the editor will be to select material fed on to film, rather in the way that a television producer in his control room selects the picture to go out over the TV screens from a number of alternatives being taken simultaneously by cameras in the studio. Computers also have a big role to play in controlling the handling and distribution of newspapers to wholesalers and newsagents.

Current technology can measure, by electronic means, colour and ink balance far more accurately than the human judgement on which printers have relied hitherto. Looking a little further ahead, electrostatic printing machines may obviate the need for printing plates, and so enable a much greater degree of copy flexibility. These machines can print on to all kinds of surface, and can print from images displayed on a cathode ray tube. This means that printing can be stored on videotape.

The application of these inventions – all of which have been made and proved – will not only lead to much greater printing productivity and flexibility. They will transform the industry from a craft dependent on human skill and fallibility into a technology dependent on science. (In any event, as the speed of the machines increases, the application of human judgement to such things as colour register or the even balance of ink becomes increasingly impossible, so that electronic control becomes essential if standards are to be maintained.) Today's craftsman must therefore become tomorrow's technologist, and management too will need higher standards of technical qualification. The industry will need fewer but much more highly paid workers, and the union structure will be transformed as many of the existing crafts become obsolete. While the small printer may well survive on a jobbing basis, among the bigger firms there will almost certainly be amalgamations and financial concentration to take advantage of the new capital-intensive techniques. The fact that an increasing number of concerns have been recently buying their way into the industry from outside is likely to accelerate this structural revolution. It is significant that in the United States in the last few years there has been a trend towards mergers and financial tie-ups between electronics firms and printers and publishers.

All this, to repeat, simply involves the application of knowledge which has been available for several years. Yet productivity in the industry has been going up very slowly indeed in recent years; in the five years 1958–63 it is estimated to have risen by no more than 4 per cent. During the same period profits have fallen and costs have risen. How does one explain the discrepancy between promise and achievement?

The explanation lies in the structure of the industry. A large proportion of printing firms, as mentioned above, are small – often family – concerns. In general printing in 1964 over 60 per

cent of all firms had under 25 operatives, and only 2·7 per cent
had more than 300. The standard of technical awareness and
professionalism is on average low, and there is a dearth of middle
management. Printing management represents one of the sur-
viving strongholds of the cult of the amateur. Both the 'know-
how' and – in many cases, though clearly not all – the capital,
are lacking for successful innovation. (The national newspapers,
who should be setting the pace, and have the resources to do so,
are for the most part particularly weak on production engineering
in their management structures.)[5]

Similarly, printing customers have so far been reluctant to
pre-plan their requirements or to accept the degree of variety
reduction (for example, by standardization of paper sizes on the
Continental pattern) which would enable automated equipment
to work long enough runs to pay its way. Clearly there must always be a jobbing element in printing; therefore there will always
be a place for the small, relatively low-capitalized firm. But the
jobbing element in the total product-mix is today unnecessarily
high, and is retarding technical progress. What is required is
more forward planning by customers, and a greater drive by the
printing industry to make it worth their while to do so. If
customers are to accept standardization, they need a price
incentive.

So both the first two major species of obstacles to innovation
mentioned above – those due to management, and those due to
the market – apply in full measure to printing. Unfortunately
the third major obstacle – that due to manpower – applies also,
in an extreme form. We will deal with this general problem in
the next chapter, but its particular application to printing is
worth a brief mention here, since it is impossible to understand
the printers' problems without it.

As was pointed out above, printing is the craft industry *par
excellence*. The craft unions control the industry tightly. They
have been able to maintain their position by restricting intake of
apprentices, and by imposing rigid job demarcations which

limit the flexibility with which labour can be used. Jobs which are essentially unskilled or semi-skilled, and which in the Netherlands for example are done by female labour, in Britain remain the preserve of the (all-male) craft unions. The Royal Commission on the Press in 1962 calculated that certain national newspapers were overstaffed in their production and distribution departments by over 30 per cent. Over the years, in order to ensure jobs for themselves, the craft unions have built up a network of restrictive practices. The report of the National Board for Prices and Incomes in 1965 gave the following examples:[6]

(a) Demarcation, particularly between craft and non-craft unions. Thus a union may insist that messages must be carried and floors swept by a craftsman; paper being transferred from one department to another may change hands at a line drawn on the floor; a machine minder may decline to carry out certain tasks, such as cleaning, on a machine in his care, and in other cases he may not be allowed to – for instance, a non-craft union has the traditional right to push buttons on a craft-controlled machine. Even within some individual unions there are strict limits between different categories of work, and men temporarily surplus in one section may not transfer to another.

(b) Restrictions on upgrading. It is difficult, and sometimes impossible, for machine assistants to graduate to become machine minders even though they are sufficiently skilled. In one union there is an annual quota for probationers to be accepted for upgrading over a period of three years.

(c) Overmanning. Where there are batteries of printing machines, or batteries of printing units in one machine, it would often be possible to reduce the manning. Thus, where one assistant may be needed on one machine, only six may be needed on twelve machines, but in fact twelve are employed.

(d) Pegged outputs. Outputs on various machines and other operations such as packing parcels are controlled to fixed, maximum limits well below the reasonable potential. In other cases fixed times are taken for such duties as oiling and cleaning machines, irrespective of the varying circumstances.

(*e*) Other restrictions include the imposition of rotas for over-time which result in people being paid for work they have not done; the traditional working day starting later and finishing earlier than the official times; and the control by one union of the transfer of men from one company to another.

The report goes on:

One of the characteristics of the industry is that an employer installing a new type of machine in his factory may find that he will have to do so without having any clear notion of how many men will be employed on it and what extra payments he will have to make to those that are employed. He awaits joint inspection and rating, *after* the machine has been installed, by representatives of the British Federation of Master Printers and the union concerned. There is no satisfactory procedure for resolving any dispute, with the result that machines can sometimes be installed for months or even years without being brought into production.

The N.B.P.I. was told by employers that, given a more economical use of labour, performance could be improved by anything from 10 to 25 per cent from existing equipment, while with new equipment – to which the situation outlined above is plainly a major deterrent – the gains could be considerably greater. The report, rightly, does not acquit the employers of some share in the responsibility for this sorry state of affairs – but, whoever is to blame, it is clearly not conducive to cooperative innovation. It is fair to point out that, while examples of one or other of the practices listed above can be found in a wide range of British industry (particularly in the older industries like shipbuilding, docks, and some sectors of engineering), probably nowhere but in printing – and there by no means in all firms – does one find so grave an accumulation of restrictive practices. It is also fair to say that a similar situation exists, in some degree, in many other printing industries – though by no means in all, and probably in none to so serious an extent as in Britain. (The Americans, for example, have had major difficulties with the printing unions over newspaper automation – but they *have* made progress nevertheless.)

The industry is now, belatedly, making a strenuous effort to put its house in order through a system of joint manpower committees on which both management and unions are represented. But the trade union obstacle to innovation is more fundamental than the existence of restrictive practices and an uncooperative atmosphere. The technical changes discussed above would not only lead to a need for fewer workers; they would sweep away the whole justification for the existing structure of printing crafts, on which the union system is based. This is an extreme case of what we shall see in the next chapter is a general obstacle to innovation. The craftsman derives his strength and his status and wage differential from his possession of certain skills which are needed in the current state of technology. Alter the technology, and the basis of his superior position is destroyed. At worst, he faces technological unemployment; at best, he must adapt to a new system of work in which he no longer enjoys his former premium. Inevitably, therefore, he tends to resist change, and to insure himself against it by the kind of restrictions at which the printing craftsmen have proved themselves so adept. In the long term, of course, this type of self-defence is unsustainable. But before that position is reached, enormous harm may have been done. Any attempt at planned innovation must, therefore, reckon with the necessity of buying out or otherwise accommodating the craftsman. Methods of doing this will be discussed in the next chapter.

## Building – Craft or System?

The most important industry still operating on a predominantly craft basis in Britain and other highly industrialized countries is building. It is also a major bottleneck industry, and looks like continuing to be so. Demand for construction rose in the United Kingdom, despite fluctuations, by an annual average of 3·7 per cent between 1956 and 1964. The National Plan forecast an annual increase from 1964 to 1970 of 4·6 per cent per annum, and it was widely held in 1965 that this was too modest a rate for the needs of Britain's social infrastructure. But during the first two years of the Labour administration before the big cut-back of July 1966 the industry was showing all the signs of overstrain, with acute shortages of skilled workers, as well as of management and many types of professional skill – not to mention certain types of building material. The industry already employs nearly two million workers, and the reserves of extra labour available under full employment conditions are very small. Any increase in demand must therefore be met primarily out of extra productivity, and this requires new and more efficient working methods.

Nor can one readily adjust the demand for construction to the available capacity by the application of 'stop–go' methods. In the first place, as we have seen, the modernization of Britain's industrial structure requires a great deal of social and infra-structure investment, which must fall heavily on the construc-tion industry. Second, improvement in productivity requires continuity in ordering – for reasons which will become apparent below. In construction, therefore, more than in most industries improvements in the efficiency of supply are absolutely un-avoidable. The modernization of Britain requires as a prior condition the modernization of construction.

As it happens, building – like printing – is on the verge of a technological revolution. This is what is known as 'industrial-ized' or 'systems' building.[7] Industrialized building involves the use of standardized prefabricated components which can be produced on a factory production line and assembled on-site by unskilled labour using mechanical equipment – in place of the use of traditional materials assembled by skilled workers using manual labour, as in conventional building methods. Industrialized building saves time, on-site labour – particularly skilled labour – and professional skills. The greater the propor-tion of our building that can be done by industrialized methods, therefore, the more likely we are to be able to achieve the overall productivity increase which is needed. Some of the productivity increases and time-saving claimed for industrialized methods are very substantial indeed, ranging up to 50 per cent or more on saving of site manpower. If the nation is to achieve its target of 500,000 houses a year by 1970, at least one in five – and possibly as much as one in three – will need to be built by industrialized methods. Two years ago the proportion so built was around one in fifteen.

This is not just a British phenomenon. The same problems of growing needs and traditional building technologies face practically all the advanced countries, and in each the response has been broadly similar. Prefabrication of small components – ready-made window frames, kitchen fittings, internal partitions and the like – is now common in most countries. The next stage is the use of prefabricated structural elements – complete walls and floors, sometimes whole rooms. Russia has been experimenting with the transfer of prefabricated concrete rooms from factory to site by helicopter. Throughout Eastern Europe, blocks of flats and other buildings are made from large concrete panels. In France, more than 10 per cent of all new dwellings are made from concrete-based systems, while a further 10 per cent use other types of industrialized systems.

Unfortunately the economics of systems building are far from straightforward. As with any substitution of capital for labour, the break-even point is raised and full economy of working requires large, standardized orders over a fairly long period of time. The situation is exactly analogous to that described above for printing. An initial capital investment is needed to pay for the factory to make the components. Moreover, since these are for the most part very bulky, the transport costs become prohibitive unless the factory is within easy reach of the building sites where its products will be used. For heavy components transport costs become prohibitive above fifty miles.

There are a great many different systems in use, each differing in the type of materials and the degree of capital intensity. But the principle is the same for all, in greater or lesser degree. Systems building cannot compete with traditional building if orders come in small lots; it cannot operate on a jobbing, 'one-off' basis. To meet the initial investment, a systems builder must be able to achieve significant economies of large scale; this means a large order throughput on a constant basis over a reasonable period of time. Repetitiveness and continuity of ordering are essential.

It follows that the first requirement for systems building is to organize the market to enable these conditions to be met. The great bulk of the market for systems building is in the public sector. Only some 2 per cent of private houses are built by these methods. The reason is obvious. Only public authorities are normally in a position to place orders in large enough quantities over long enough periods to make industrialized methods competitive. It is also significant that the greatest progress in systems building in this country has been in the school building programme, where the same conditions apply.

However, even in the public sector the proportion of houses and other buildings built by industrialized systems has tended to lag behind that in many Continental countries. One reason for this is the greater proportion of multi-storey flats, which lend themselves most readily to industrialized systems, on the Continent. Another reason has been the fragmentation of local authority organization in this country. There are some 1,400 local authorities in Britain today and several hundred separate planning authorities, and these constitute the ultimate customer for public sector housing. The average size of council-house contract was until recently under 50 dwellings. By contrast, the Communist countries with their very high degree of imposed standardization have been able to move ahead much faster with industrialized building methods. And in Western Europe, too, standardization has gone further than in Britain. In Sweden the average local authority contract in 1938 was for twenty dwellings. Today it is for ten times as many.

The promotion of industrialized building has, therefore, become a matter for government in this country. Only government can provide the economic climate which will facilitate continuity in orders. Moreover, the public sector provides about half the total market for the construction industry, and for this the government is ultimately responsible. The government has to plan investment on roads, schools and hospitals several years in advance. In addition, through the Ministry of Public Building and Works and more recently the Ministry of Housing, it has perforce found itself involved in what is arguably the most far-reaching drive to promote innovation in a single industry to be found in Britain today – partly, but by no means exclusively, by attempting to influence the structure of the market.

The first objective has been to try to group together local authorities into large enough buying consortia to meet the necessary requirements. This has been only partly successful, and rather more success is being reached by the alternative method of grouping manufacturers together into consortia to pool supply contracts. One of the problems is ignorance on the part of most local authorities as to the merits of rival systems. There is at present a bewildering number of systems on the market or projected – about four hundred in all; not much more than 10 per cent of these are likely to prove ultimately viable, and big sums of money have been lost by some incautious venturers in this field of manufacture. There is an urgent need for standardization on a limited number of systems, and much work needs to be done on evaluating rival systems and advising local authorities and other prospective clients as to their relative merits. The National Building Agency, set up to advise local authorities on systems building, has been investigating systems and issuing appraisal certificates for those found satisfactory.

The local authorities' suspicions about industrialized building should also be partly allayed by the adoption in 1965 of the French *Agrément* system, whereby houses built by ministry-approved systems are insured for the first ten years of their life by the state. This was also designed to help reduce the inhibitions which some building societies are said to harbour against advancing mortgages on industrialized houses.

Greater standardization of building inevitably requires the standardization of building regulations, which have hitherto been governed by local by-laws varying from area to area. As a result of legislation by the Conservative administration, the government can now lay down national building regulations. But more needs to be done to sweep away the present jungle of statutory provisions and rationalize the administration of local planning controls.

Advantage is being taken of the move to a metric system in building to achieve a much greater standardization of dimensions and equipment and components, and to reduce variety. If the report of the Royal Commission currently sitting on Local Government leads – as many hope – to a drastic reduction in the number of separate local authorities in England and Wales, industrialized building will probably be enabled to take another major leap forward.

Continuity of ordering is not only important in justifying the initial investment required for systems building. It is also necessary in enabling builders to undertake forward planning, to carry out the necessary training and to build up appropriate management teams, design staffs and so on. If the building craft unions are going to be brought to accept the new methods, with their inevitable impact on the long-term demand for their own skills, they will need some assurance as to the future. This can only be given on the basis of effective forward planning.

I came across an example of this a few years ago in Northern Ireland. There, despite the high unemployment rate, construction projects which would bring new work to the population were being held up because of a shortage of bricklayers. This was due to restrictions on intake imposed by the bricklayers' union. The motivation was fear of unemployment, which was understandable – if hardly commendable – in view of the overall employment position in Ulster. In fact, however, it was plainly self-defeating, since it was merely holding up economic development; and the province's work programme should have been enough to ensure full employment for the bricklayers for many years ahead. In these circumstances the sensible thing would have been to offer the bricklayers guaranteed employment for a fixed period if they would agree to relax restrictions on entry. But this could only be done on the basis of forward planning of demand.

(I do not wish to give the impression that the attitude of the unions is a major obstacle to industrialization of building. It is not. Indeed, compared with the printing unions, their attitude to change has been reasonably co-operative. The main obstacles lie elsewhere.)

In its submission to the National Plan, the industry stressed the need for more adequate research, for more rapid progress on standardization, and for rapid implementation of the reforms in tendering procedure advocated in the 1964 Banwell Report. But its main emphasis was placed on

the need for an improvement and extension of the programming of work in the public sector, not only in broad terms five or more years ahead, but also in detail two or three years ahead. In order to achieve such detailed planning, it may be necessary to introduce a minimum of a three-year accounting period in central and local government. The detailed programmes in the public sector must be available to allow adequate time for the design of projects. Design work is often held up by delays in obtaining planning consents and in consequence is often rushed. . . . Both building and civil engineering have stressed the advantages of programming a project before work on site begins and are well aware of the need to improve site management by the use of the more advanced techniques now available. Improvement in organization is required at each stage of the construction process, but it is very often dependent on early consultation and co-operation between the various participants in a project and especially on closer links between the processes of design and construction.

The switch from traditional to industrialized building methods puts new demands on management. A much higher degree of planning and programming is required, involving on larger contracts the use of advanced scheduling techniques like network analysis. Failure to appreciate this has led to disappointing results in more than one past incursion into systems building.

Longer-term planning of programmes, and placing of orders in large or repetitive units, enables firms to use their design staff more productively, to place orders for materials and components in bulk, to plan the construction process further in advance, to invest in more plant, more training and more management, and to use their existing manpower more efficiently. Most of these benefits apply whether industrialized or traditional methods are used, but for the economic use of industrialized methods they are essential.

All this requires, however, certain changes in the traditional method of tendering for building orders, as recommended in the Banwell Report. If builders have to tender anew for each order they find it difficult to achieve the continuity which we have seen to be so desirable. The Ministry of Housing has been concerned to negotiate regional price agreements between some system sponsors and local authority groups, based on cost analyses provided by the sponsors and validated by the ministry. Moreover, the separation of design work from production frequently prevents the use of the most economical methods of construction. What is needed is for all those involved in the project – client, architect, quantity surveyor, contractor – to work in co-operation from a very early stage, so that the operation can be planned jointly. The attitude of the architects in particular to this has been somewhat mixed. Some see a threat to their status and independence in too close an association with the building contractor, and a loss of freedom in having to work within the discipline of an industrialized system. Others see it as an inevitable development, and indeed as a creative challenge.

Since most builders tend to be short of working capital, regular progress payments are desirable if enough investment is to be undertaken in new plant and new methods.

The development of systems building, and the difficulties it has encountered, illustrate graphically the 'spill-over' effects of changes in technology; in this case they affect not only almost every aspect of the industry itself, but because of the peculiar nature of the industry and its market they have involved the organization and structure of local government and its relations with central government. Nor, indeed, have these effects yet worked their way fully through. It seems clear that, as systems building develops, the medium-sized building firm is going to find itself increasingly squeezed between the large firms with their proprietary systems on the one hand, and on the other the small builder who will continue to concentrate on 'one-off' jobs and repair and maintenance work. There may therefore be an accelerated trend towards polarization in this industry.

But will even the repair and maintenance side of building remain indefinitely immune from the 'systems revolution'? With the growth of plastics in building – probably the greatest growth area for this range of materials in the next few years – and the growing use of prefabricated units (packaged central heating systems in place of fireplaces, prefabricated bathrooms instead of baths), it seems clear that even within the ambit of conventional building there is going to be increasing use of standardized, prefabricated components. Building technology is clearly in a revolutionary phase.

The task of diffusing new technology through such a vast, ramifying industry is proving enormously complex. On the one hand government is theoretically in a strong position to impose its will since it controls the finance for the 50 per cent or more of the market which lies in the public sector. On the other hand the practical autonomy enjoyed by the local authorities is considerable. And on the supply side, the chain of intermediaries is exceptionally long and the structure of the industry particu-

larly daunting. This is an industry of some 90,000 separate
firms, about a quarter of whom are one-man businesses, and
only two hundred of whom employ more than five hundred
operatives apiece.

After considerable difficulties and frustrations, the drive to
promote systems building has recently begun to enjoy an
encouraging degree of success. In the first half of 1966 the
proportion of local authorities' tenders for industrialized
dwellings rose to 36 per cent – compared with 20 per cent in
1964; this is very near the National Plan target ratio for 1970 of
40 per cent. (But this target ratio is now thought to have been
too small.)

But it has not been by any means a painless process, nor is
success yet guaranteed. The experience of the last few years
shows, indeed, the difficulty of changing established patterns
and attitudes in industry, the professions and local government.
How much more difficult must government's problem be
where it has no significant buying power, and no obvious scope
for influencing the market!

## The Management of Innovation

The management of innovation is plainly one of the most
complex of all the problems facing the nation and the individual
firm. In the modern market economy products have a natural
life-cycle: novelty, acceptance, familiarity, obsolescence
(whether due to technological or market factors). If a company
is to prosper it must have the bulk of its turnover in products
which are at the profitable phase of their life-cycle, so that when
one item in the product range passes into obsolescence there are
others to take its place. A dynamic product-planning policy is
therefore essential in a world of consumer affluence and
accelerating technology.

But this is much easier said than done. Experience shows
that technological innovation does not necessarily lead by itself

to profitability. Indeed, without effective management – particularly in the marketing and cost control fields – an adventurous policy of product innovation can lead to commercial disaster. The failure rate on new products is bound, by the nature of things, to be high. Risk-free innovation is a contradiction in terms. Half the products test-marketed in Britain never get beyond their test area. Even in the United States the failure rate on new products has been as high as 90 per cent over four years.[8]

Nor can there be any rules the following of which guarantees success (though there *are* procedures which will almost guarantee failure!). There is no 'right' proportion of a firm's or a country's budget to devote to R. & D. and no 'right' allocation between basic and applied research, 'in-firm' and collective research, and so on. Germany and Japan have both devoted, in recent years, a much smaller proportion of national product to R. & D. than Britain; but their record in innovation has been significantly better. This is not because we have been bad at discovering things. We have, however, been rather bad at applying what we and others have discovered. Moreover, like the Americans, we have concentrated a large proportion of our research on the defence industries, and the fall-out from these on civil technology has been comparatively small.

It seems clear that, as a nation, we need to think more carefully about ways of disseminating information – particularly from the research stations and research associations – and this requires a higher priority in government plans for boosting innovation. It is also clear that more thinking needs to be done on the role of the research associations, and on improving their efficiency. Many research associations need more money if they are to do their job properly, and if they are to disseminate enough information about their activities. A large proportion of this money needs to come from industry, and the most obvious method for increasing industry's subscriptions is by a compulsory levy (as is being done for training). This does not, of course, rule out the possibility of further financial assistance from government, particularly for special research projects. Finally, it is to be hoped that the reappraisal now going on in the Ministry of Technology will embrace the proposal in the F.B.I. report of 1963 for amalgamations of research associations and groupings on a common campus. Not only is this an obvious form of rationalization, but it should promote the cross-fertilization of ideas which we have seen to be essential for successful innovation. Such campuses might, in a modest way, do the same kind of job that, as we saw in the last chapter, M.I.T. and other similar institutions have done in the United States – namely, provide the nucleus or sparking-plug for 'the critical mass of research-based industries' which Britain needs.

But, however efficient and dynamic the institutions for collective research become, effective innovation must predominantly take place inside the firm. Such innovation requires, first, constructive liaison between those concerned with basic research (whether in, or more commonly outside, the firm) and those concerned with its application. The latter must, in turn, as we saw in Chapter 2, be in tune with what is going on or being planned elsewhere in the enterprise.

Companies have to decide, in the light of their resources and their overall product and market strategy, how big an 'in-firm' research effort they should undertake, and of what kind. In recent years there has been a tendency for some of the leading British firms to opt out of fundamental research, and to try to relate their R. & D. effort more closely to the specific objectives of the enterprise. Given the traditional weighting of basic to applied research in the British system, and the wealth of institutions available for collective research in this country, this is almost certainly a sensible development. But, of course, the wider the sphere of interests of the company, the more variegated its product base, the greater the latitude and flexibility it must give to its R. & D. people. The need for the functional approach must always be borne in mind.

Various formulae have been devised from time to time to enable a company to assess the 'right' proportion of its resources to invest in research. One approach is to assess how long the company could last – what its 'life' would be – if it stopped research altogether. This can be assessed very roughly by examining the company's product range at fixed periods in the past and estimating how many of these products could be sold now if no research had been invested in them. The shorter the company's 'life' on this method of assessment, the greater the justifiable investment in R. & D. in relation to total resources.

A more common method is for companies to divide their research programme into three broad headings. First, there is fundamental research, which as we have seen tends if anything to be a declining element so far as corporate R. & D. is concerned. Second, there is 'defensive' research, aimed at making existing products and processes more competitive. This kind of expenditure, being mainly a matter of cost reductions and specific product improvements, is normally susceptible to fairly realistic calculations about the scope for worthwhile research, and it is usually the least prone to fluctuations resulting from executive decisions or cash flow changes. The third type of R. & D. investment is 'offensive' research aimed at developing new products and processes. This is the most difficult area of decision, and the one where expenditures tend to fluctuate most, depending on overall corporate strategies, the dynamism or otherwise of boards of directors, the need (real or believed) for new products, the availability of capital – not only for the research, but for exploitation of the products of research. (It is plainly pointless to spend money on inventing new products if one lacks the resources to bring them into profitable production once invented.)

The problem of adequate appraisal of R. & D. programmes by companies, on the lines of the 'technical audit' described in Chapter 2, is receiving growing attention from leading British firms. Some concerns, both in the United Kingdom and United

States, have special 'programme appraisal staffs' within the R. & D. organization, to carry out a permanent internal technical audit. Some companies, like Richard Thomas & Baldwins in this country, use their O.R. departments to carry out this task. Most concerns on both sides of the Atlantic would probably however agree that 'research into research' needs to be further refined and developed before they can be reasonably sure that they are getting an adequate return from their investment in R. & D.

The development of a new product requires the closest cooperation between the R. & D. team, the design team, production and marketing. Design is not, of course, simply a question of increasing the visual attraction of the product. The designer must concern himself with questions of cost and function. Where machinery is involved, he must pay regard to ergonomic factors to ensure that the machine maximizes effectiveness while minimizing fatigue for the operator. To keep down costs he needs to apply value analysis or similar techniques, and in particular to see whether existing components can be used to save the cost of making specials; the use of Brisch references (which catalogue items of equipment by function and description) is particularly useful here.

At least equally important is integration between product development and marketing. Before development a new product must be adequately appraised in commercial terms. One way of doing this is by the technique of Qualitative Product Screening.[9] This involves an evaluation of the requirements of the product if it is to make profits, and the ability of the firm to provide those requirements. On the one hand one has to list the company's resources, on the other the calls the product will make on them and the possible contributions it might make to them. As many as 30 or 40 factors may enter into such an inventory, including such things as the product's marketability, growth prospects, the permanence of its market, the adequacy of the firm's production and development facilities, and so on.

Each factor is then ascribed a numerical weight against which the new product is scored. From this emerges a product 'profile', which can be compared with average scores, with the profiles of alternative new products under consideration, or with existing competitors in the market.

For such screening to result in accurate profiles, of course, the firm must have some experience in market research. This is a field in which, compared with the United States, British industry – because management has traditionally been production-rather than market-oriented – has tended to be backward. There has been a tendency in too much of British industry in the past to assume that if the product is good enough it is bound to sell, and to regard market research – particularly for capital equipment – as a species of gimmickry. (The attitude towards market research is perhaps the most significant index of the difference between the amateur and the professional manager. In a remarkable number of cases in my experience amateur managements will swallow far more dubious or marginal techniques, yet jib at market research as being 'a waste of money'.) The result is, in too many cases, the loss of contact between supplier and customer which we discussed, in the engineering context, in the last chapter. Fortunately, with the improvement in management standards, the use of market research and other modern marketing techniques is growing, and there is much closer integration than in the past between R. & D., design, production and marketing. But, though the position is improving, it could still be better.

Finally, if it is to get the best value out of its R. & D., a company must know when to kill off its failures. As we saw in Chapter 2, there is again no golden rule for this, and different companies adopt very different policies. Nevertheless, some form of financial controls need to be used, with a 'cut-off' at the point where it becomes clear that further expenditure on a project would simply involve waste of resources to no purpose.

I.C.I. has employed the following system. For other than

'defensive' R. & D. expenditure, there is a ceiling of £20,000 per project, above which figure sanction is required from head office or the appropriate divisional board. This means that if a scientist wishes to start a new line of inquiry he needs nobody's approval but his immediate superior's. But once the cumulative expenditure on the project has begun to become significant, higher management gets interested. As I.C.I.'s former research director told me: 'You can start with something apparently quite crazy, but you must apply progressively stricter controls as the expenditure, the time and the experience builds up.'

I am not saying that this is necessarily the right formula – or indeed that any formula can be proved 'right'. But no company can afford to undertake R. & D. if it is not prepared to face the fact that most of its projects will be failures, and to devise techniques for recognizing and disposing of them. Life, unfortunately, is like that.

NOTES TO CHAPTER SIX

1. For a useful study of the attitudes of British management, see the P.E.P. study *Thrusters and Sleepers* (Allen & Unwin, 1965. Published under the title *Attitudes in British Management* by Penguin Books, 1966).

2. The head of Emerson's British operation until recently was Mr William W. Allen (see page 34).

3. H.M.S.O., Cmnd 2937.

4. A glossary of some of the main management techniques, including a number not referred to in this book, is contained in the April and September 1966 issues of *Management Today*. See also *Glossary of Management Techniques* by H.M. Treasury (H.M.S.O., 1967) and *Spreading Ideas to Raise Productivity: a Glossary of Techniques* by the British Productivity Council.

5. The newspaper industry has its own problems, which were spelt out graphically at the beginning of 1967 in a report by the Economist Intelligence Unit for the industry's joint board headed by Lord Devlin. The E.I.U. puts the blame for the industry's troubles primarily on the amateurishness of most newspaper managements – an analysis endorsed by the E.D.C. for Newspapers, Printing and Publishing. The effects of managerial failure to cope with a situation of rapid technological and market change are revealed in frightening detail in this report.

6. H.M.S.O., Cmnd 2750.

7. For a useful discussion of the problems of industrialized building, see *The Industrialization of Building*, a report of the Royal Institute of British Architects (April 1965).

8. See 'Conditions Favourable to Product Innovation', by David Ashton, Russell Gotham and Gordon Wills, *Scientific Business* (May 1965). I have made extensive use of this article in this section of the chapter.

9. See 'Selecting New Products for Development', by Aubrey Wilson, *Scientific Business* (November 1963).

# CHAPTER SEVEN

# THE ORGANIZATION OF CHANGE

INNOVATION involves change, and there is something in human nature which is resistant to change – particularly change imposed from outside. If we are going to exploit the opportunities of technology successfully, we have to secure acceptance of change by all sectors of the community, and particularly by the working population. But we have to do more than that. We have to promote the mobility of labour to a far greater extent than in the past; and we have to provide enough of the new ranges of skills which are going to be required. None of these is going to be easy; each is going to be essential.

The impact of automation on the job structure, as we have already seen, is extremely radical. It is not just that far fewer workers are required to produce the same number of goods. Whole categories of skill are liable to disappear as technology changes, and to be replaced by new categories altogether. In particular, the craftsman is liable to be replaced by the technician or technologist over a very wide range of industry. This has radical implications for the trade union structure. In Sweden and in most of the Continental countries, most trade unions are organized on an industrial basis; that is, they group together all workers in a given industry, regardless of levels of skill. In the United States the C.I.O. (Congress of Industrial Organizations) group of unions are organized on an industrial basis, the older A.F. of L. (American Federation of Labor) unions on a craft basis. In Britain, although some industrial unions do exist, the common basis of union organization is by craft, with unskilled workers over a very wide range of industries and occupations being grouped together in one or other of the two 'general' workers' unions, the Transport and General

Workers Union (T. & G.W.U.), and the National Union of General and Municipal Workers (N.U.G.M.W.).

In most British industries, therefore, trade union representation is divided among a number of different unions, supporting different sectional interests, and with one large group – the craft unions – having a strong vested interest in the technological status quo. This is a very powerful obstacle to change – particularly as, unlike the Swedish unions, the British trade unions acknowledge little practical allegiance to their central organization, the T.U.C. Efforts to modernize and rationalize the union structure, and to provide for more centralization of authority in the movement, have in the past proved depressingly unsuccessful. An incomes policy which worked, under which the T.U.C. was recognized as the sole accredited spokesman and negotiator for the unions, would almost certainly in course of time produce a Swedish-type situation in Britain – and, as we have seen, some tentative steps are now being taken along this road. The T.U.C. would then be in a position to carry out the internal reforms which are required in the unions, and to turn them – as in Sweden – into positive forces for change, rather than the obstacles that they too frequently are today. For it is plain that the long-term interest of the union movement *as a whole*, quite as much as of the rest of us, lies in successful innovation rather than in an attempt to preserve the status quo at all costs.

Nor is this simply a question of reorganizing the unions into groups which correspond more closely to the industrial structure of the 1960s and 1970s than to that of the 1920s. It is a question, also, of improving the internal organization of the unions, to reduce the present appalling gap in communications between leaders and rank-and-file. Only when this has been remedied will the union leadership be able to steer its members in a positive direction. It is also urgently necessary to bridge the gulf in social attitudes between management and worker, to end the 'We–They' dichotomy, under which any action which might seem to benefit one side is automatically thought to be likely to damage the other. I believe that this class barrier, which seems to be so depressingly strong still in Britain, is a reflection of a sense of weakness on the part of the workers, and that a stronger, more coherent, more positively aggressive union movement would do more than anything else to ease it. Until it *is* eased it will prove very difficult to secure the co-operation which will enable change to take place peacefully and harmoniously, at the accelerated pace which the onset of automation is going to require.[1]

In default of trade union reform, a greater burden has to be borne by government and management. Government has to try to create a climate in which change can take place with the minimum of friction. Its approach to labour relations has to be dynamic, geared to the overriding necessity of improving efficiency and securing a better use of resources. The old static concept of the function of the Ministry of Labour – as a kind of referee to hold the ring between labour and management, and intervene when one or the other cried 'foul' – has gone for ever. Never again can a Minister of Labour pretend to neutrality between dynamism and sloth, between the progressive and the stagnant side. Change must be supported, even if it brings strife in its train, provided that the end result is greater efficiency. The test of good labour relations today is not whether or not a plant is strike-free, but whether or not management can persuade its workers to accept the changes which it believes to be necessary for greater efficiency. By these standards the labour relations of the National Coal Board in recent years have been a considerable success (despite the continuing problem of absenteeism) – much better than those of some other concerns with many fewer strikes on their record. There is a world of difference between the peaceful acceptance of change and the peaceful enjoyment of stagnation.

## How to 'De-man'

As we saw in Chapter 1, manpower – particularly skilled manpower – is one of Britain's scarcest resources; it is also one of the most wastefully used. We have already seen how badly our manning scales in certain key industries compare with those in America, and in certain cases with the Continent. Youngstown Sheet and Tube in the United States employs 95 people to produce £1 million worth of steel; Stewarts & Lloyds in the United Kingdom employs 259. Du Pont, in the United States, employs 101 men to produce £1 million worth of chemicals; I.C.I. employs 167. Volkswagen in Germany employs 75 men to produce £1 million worth of vehicles; B.M.C. in the United Kingdom employs 82.[2] These are all large companies which should have full and equal access to the latest technology. How can one explain the discrepancy?

Partly, no doubt, it arises from different sizes of plant, and from greater standardization in the foreign plants; Volkswagen certainly produces fewer models than B.M.C., for example. Partly it reflects a lower state of awareness on the part of British management in the past of the need to reduce manning scales. Also, to a considerable extent, it reflects trade union practices and attitudes in this country compared with those abroad. In Sweden, for example, the unions encourage the maximum flexibility of workers between different production-line jobs in order to raise productivity and therefore wages. In Britain each craft tends to guard its job privileges jealously, and to resist any crossing of demarcation lines (as we saw, developed to a grotesque extent, in the N.B.P.I. report on printing in the last chapter).

Perhaps the biggest reservoir of underemployed labour in Britain today exists among the class of craftsman's mate. There are more than 500,000 such workers in British industry today, or 2½ per cent of the total labour force. Mr Allen of Emerson has described them as 'an anthropological status symbol existing solely to carry the craftsman's tools, costing Britain perhaps £500 million a year'.[3] Allen and other efficiency experts reckon that if all these 500,000 were to be paid off it would have no adverse effect on productivity at all – provided the craftsman were prepared to carry his own tools and do the other menial jobs which the mate currently performs for him.

Flexibility between crafts, and the elimination of the craftsman's mate, are the two chief ingredients in the 'productivity bargains' which more and more British firms – following the pattern established by Allen at Fawley[4] – are now seeking to negotiate with their unions. This practice is described by the Americans – who have had more experience of it than we have – as 'buying the union rule book'. Wage increases, and where appropriate job security promises, are traded against the abolition of traditional agreements which limit the efficient use of labour. Not only do such agreements, where successful, produce dramatic increases in productivity. They have also enabled many firms to reduce the incidence of overtime – a peculiarly costly and inefficient method of working, which has been inflated in post-war Britain by the artificial shortage of labour.

Productivity bargaining may not, however, be as easy as it sounds. It requires very careful planning by management in advance, and intensive policing afterwards. Management must know exactly what it wants to get, and how much it is worth paying to get it. This involves establishing, by work study, inter-firm comparisons, and other means, what rational manning scales – as distinct from those that have grown up by custom – for particular operations should be. Further, it involves carrying out detailed forecasting of manpower needs over a period of some years ahead – particularly if the 'package' includes pledges on job security. Manpower planning of this kind is something which few British firms or industries have ever undertaken in the past on any significant scale. Then, since most productivity bargains involve large outlays of money by the employer – no union sells its rule book cheaply – they require some very careful calculations of expected productivity gains before the negotiations start. Finally, the idea of abandoning traditional working arrangements for the sake of greater efficiency has to be sold carefully and skilfully to the workers – particularly if more than one union is involved. And after the agreement is concluded, great care is required over a long period to make sure that the old practices are not creeping back, that the flexibility that was bought is in fact being delivered. In short, successful productivity bargains require not only good labour relations, but a high standard of management ability.

Productivity bargains are also much easier to strike in an expanding economic climate, and in a firm or industry where the wage structure is relatively simple. Complex wage structures can make bargaining almost impossibly difficult, while in a deflationary climate workers become increasingly attached to traditional practices which are thought to protect jobs. It is also obviously easier for an employer to undertake the necessary forward planning, and to enter into forward commitments on employment, if the economic barometer for his organization is set fair. It is no accident that most of the pioneers in pro-ductivity bargaining have been growth industries. It is also clear that the pace at which this type of bargaining expands will to some extent be determined by the success or otherwise of the economy in achieving a reasonably steady rate of growth. 'Stop–go' could prove disastrous for productivity bargaining, at once raising the price of the rule book and reducing the employer's confidence in bidding for it.

But, if these conditions are met, there is little doubt that more and more wage bargaining will take this form. Once employers start to examine their payrolls systematically, they almost invariably discover a good deal of 'fat'. I.C.I., to take a not untypical example, recently estimated that it could produce its current output with nearly 10 per cent fewer workers. And the need to increase productivity is going to become increasingly acute over the next few years, for Britain's industrial labour force is liable to grow very slowly from now on, because of demographic trends, accentuated by the curbs on immigration and the dwindling reserves of labour on the land. Between now and 1975 Britain's labour force is in fact more likely to decline than to increase – particularly in the early seventies, when the proposed increase in the school-leaving age will lead to a quite sharp temporary reduction in numbers at work. The U.S. labour force, by contrast, will grow at an annual rate of 1·7 per cent over this whole period. Between now and 1970 Japan's will grow by 1·4 per cent a year, France's by 0·7 per cent, Italy's by 0·3 per cent. Only Germany will be as badly off as us. Her labour force will probably fall by 0·3 per cent a year to 1970, but will grow again by 0·2 per cent a year between 1970 and 1975.

Britain, therefore, looks like being short of labour for some time to come whenever the economy is being allowed to expand – automation or no automation; and the pressures to use it more efficiently are going to become increasingly acute. Moreover, if ultra-modern equipment is installed, it needs to be worked virtually round the clock to earn its keep. So there is going to be an increasing need for shift work. This, too, will require negotiation.

Many students of the British industrial scene have stressed the extent to which overtime is socially determined, arguing that workers decide roughly how much money they want to earn in the week, calculate how much overtime this will require, and adjust the pace of work during normal hours to assure themselves of the amount of overtime they have decided in advance that they want to work. There is little doubt that over large areas of industry this is a fair statement of what does actually happen, though it argues a certain weakness in management's control of the shop floor. This is a factor which clearly has to be taken into account in productivity bargains. If the worker takes overtime into his calculations in assessing his planned take-home pay, there is presumably a good deal of scope for speeding up the pace of work in normal hours by increasing the basic wage. Overtime is then available as a reserve form of capacity, so to speak, to meet an unexpected upsurge in demand. It becomes – what it always should have been – a convenience for management; rather than, as it has become, a bribe for the worker.

In some cases, of course, agreements to reduce over-manning must involve redundancies. Such agreements are plainly more difficult to work out than those for expanding enterprises, which simply involve getting more work out of the existing labour force to avoid taking on more workers. But sometimes 'de-manning' becomes essential. Indeed, unless some industries are going to release workers, it is going to be extraordinarily difficult for the new industries on which Britain's future growth depends to get started at all.

Some firms may have been deterred from striking produc-tivity bargains with their unions for fear that the reduction of manning scales to reasonable levels would create redundancy problems which would be difficult to solve. But the experience of companies like B.O.A.C. shows that it is possible, with care-ful planning, to achieve a planned run-down of the labour force and an improvement in labour flexibility at the same time. B.O.A.C. a few years ago provided a classic example of over-manning compared with the main U.S. airlines. A run-down in the labour force coupled with an improvement in productivity was necessary if the airline was to begin to get out of its heavy indebtedness to the government. Productivity agreements had to be negotiated with 17 separate unions, and this has now been done on a three-year basis in each case. At the same time the labour force had to be reduced by some 3,700 over a two-year period. Some of this could be achieved by natural wastage, but this had to be supplemented by generous redundancy payments geared to individual circumstances. The total cost of the operation was high – £8 million in wage increases for those who stayed and £1¼ million in redundancy grants for those who left.

But for B.O.A.C. it has proved a profitable operation. This bears out the view, expressed by Allen and others, that it is in most cases much cheaper for a firm to pay generous severance payments to a worker whom it does not want than to keep him on – besides being plainly in the national interest. If the paying of severance grants helps to diminish the workers' reluctance to abandon restrictive practices and accept dismissal in place of short-time when demand falls off, and induce them to accept new capital equipment and changed methods of work, then it is plainly a good investment.

To achieve a more rational use of labour clearly involves giving the worker a greater sense of security, since only if he feels secure will he be prepared to accept change and abandon traditional defensive tactics. Innovation must, of itself, create more insecurity. It is therefore very important for management to do what it can to counteract these forces. This requires long-term manpower planning, followed by long-term agreements on wages and other conditions of work, specifying job security where possible, and generous redundancy payments where necessary. The climate of industrial relations between workers and management will determine, perhaps more than any other single factor, whether innovation can be successfully carried through at the level of the individual firm or industry.

This again has certain implications for the way in which collective bargaining is carried on in this country. So far as basic wage negotiations are concerned, it looks as if we are moving into a period of greater centralization at national level, with wage agreements in individual industries increasingly related to the norms laid down in the prices and incomes policy. The corollary of this could well be a greater concentration on individual plant bargaining, on the U.S. model, to allow for the diversity of conditions from plant to plant. These negotiations, one hopes, will be increasingly based – wherever appropriate – on the productivity bargaining principle, increasingly long-term, and increasingly comprehensive, so that they provide a

genuine Contract of Service, covering all the relevant conditions of service – fringe benefits (seniority provisions, pensions, hours of work, grievance procedures, holidays, sick pay,
redundancy procedure and compensation, etc.) as well as
money wages. In this kind of climate it should be possible to
achieve complete labour flexibility, and it should also be
possible eventually to give such contracts legal sanction – thereby outlawing unofficial strikes and lockouts while the contract
is in force. Some institutions akin to the Continental Labour
Courts will be required to adjudicate on disputes on interpre-
tations of the contract, and alleged breaches of its terms. Then,
and only then, will we be fully in a position to exploit the
opportunities created by technology and automation.

## Positive Manpower Policies

Government has, of course, a major responsibility in helping
to bring this desirable state of affairs about. Its first responsibility
is to create the kind of economic climate which will facilitate
the type of development advocated above – that is, a climate of
steady growth. Its second responsibility is to complement the
work of individual employers in helping to provide workers
with a greater sense of security. The national provisions for
severance pay and wage-related unemployment and sickness
benefits are useful steps in this direction. In the long run we will
need to go farther along the road. The Contract of Service bill,
which provides a certain minimum job security, may eventually
need to be strengthened.

The government also needs to do more to promote labour
mobility. Mobility is partly a matter of easing union restrictions
on entry into new jobs. It is partly, also, a question of travel
facilities from one part of the country to another. The Ministry
of Labour already provides useful travel grants, which are
surprisingly little used. But more could be done to help job-
movers with their housing problems, which are a major de-

terrent to mobility. The case for a special Government Housing Corporation to build houses for letting in areas to which new workers are to be attracted, and to buy up houses in declining areas where necessary, is worth further examination.[5] As it is, many workers who own their own houses cannot afford to move from an area where there is no work to one where jobs are waiting, because they cannot find a buyer for their house and cannot afford to buy a new one.

A third aspect of mobility is the transferability of pensions. This affects all grades of worker up to senior management level. Non-transferable pensions are a serious impediment to the desirable movement of personnel, and government legislation to ensure that all pension rights can be fully transferred from job to job would be of considerable benefit to the national economy. (Proposals going some way in this direction have been advanced by the National Joint Advisory Council.)

Far and away the most important aspect of mobility, however, is training. In recent years Britain has seemed in danger of becoming an increasingly unskilled country. We have been exporting skilled labour and importing unskilled. Our methods of training crafts, by five-year apprenticeships, are increasingly inadequate and outdated, and make little allowance for the greater sophistication of modern teaching techniques. There have been perennial shortages of skilled workers, even at those times and in those places where unskilled men were in heavy surplus. This is a situation which cannot be allowed to continue.

In Sweden, where positive manpower policies have been developed probably to a greater extent than anywhere else, more than 1 per cent of the labour force is permanently under training in some form or another. The Swedes, with a labour force only one seventh of ours, are currently re-training four times as many people. The United States, though its efforts have so far – as we have seen – lagged behind requirements, is nevertheless a good way ahead of us. More than 100,000 a year go through the re-training courses of the Department of

Labor's Office of Automation and Manpower, and this is supplemented by a great deal of re-training and technical education elsewhere. Indeed, it has been calculated that in the United States today there are more adults being educated than schoolchildren.

In this country the position on re-training has been and remains inadequate. The main facilities for re-training are provided by government training centres, run by the Ministry of Labour. These had an annual throughput capacity of 8,000 in 1964. By 1966 this had increased to 12,800, and by the end of 1968 the G.T.C.s will be able to re-train up to 20,000 people a year. Set against the community's needs, this still seems pretty unsatisfactory. But unfortunately it is not possible to argue that the supply of G.T.C. places lags very far behind the demand for them. One limit to their expansion is set by the shortage of teachers. But a more fundamental one is that the demand for re-training facilities is not as great as it should be. This is partly because the financial inducements to a man to be re-trained are not, at least in the short term, very dazzling; and partly because the craft unions are still pretty restrictive, in some parts of the country, in their attitude to the products of G.T.C.s. We have here a complex of problems which still await solution.

If we are making less progress than we should on *re-training*, however, the position is happily much better as regards *training*. This is due to the 1964 Industrial Training Act passed by the Conservative government – one of the most important pieces of social legislation in recent years. The Act provides for each main industry to set up its own training board, financed by a compulsory levy on all firms in the industry. The boards have powers to fix their own rate of levy, and considerable discretion as to how it is spent. The Engineering Training Board, which has been more ambitious than most, has fixed its levy at $2\frac{1}{2}$ per cent of a firm's payroll; this gives it an annual income of over £75 million, to be spent on all forms of training.

The justification for the levy is that under the former system, when all training had to be carried out and paid for by individual firms, there were wide variations in the extent and quality of training offered. Some firms spent a lot of time and money on training; others saved their money, and recruited their skilled men from the firms which had trained them, by offering higher wages. Under the new scheme this is no longer feasible. All firms have to pay the levy anyway, and those firms which operate training schemes which satisfy the Board have their expenses paid out of the levy. The Board does, however, have powers of inspection to see that the money is being properly spent, and that the training is up to a high enough standard. Those firms which have good training facilities will be encouraged to undertake training on behalf of other firms in the industry, so boosting their grant. The training boards have, however, full power to supplement 'in-firm' training by other methods wherever necessary.

One essential feature of the training boards' work is to carry out very detailed manpower forecasting, to try to assess the demand over a period of years for each particular type of skill and to take steps to match the supply to the demand. They also have to consider how far present methods of training are appropriate, particularly to the new types of skill coming into demand. The development of automation could be held back to a dangerous extent by specific shortages of skills. For example, there is an acute problem of training systems analysts, whose job is to organize the work of computers in solving business problems. I.C.T. recently calculated that by 1970 Britain would need some 10,000 systems analysts; yet, it claimed, not more than two dozen or so were currently being properly trained in the United Kingdom (the emphasis here is on the word 'properly').

This is plainly a serious gap. Without adequate systems analysts it is virtually impossible for business concerns to get full value out of computers – and it is generally agreed that in

Britain today (as in the United States a few years ago) many computers are heavily underemployed, and therefore not really earning their keep. The systems analyst's task is to look at all aspects of the company's operations, and decide where and how these could usefully be handled by computer. As computer technology advances, this role is becoming increasingly complex and important. Without enough systems analysts computerization in Britain could well continue to lag, both quantitatively and qualitatively.

This is perhaps an extreme example of a new and crucial skill in short supply, but it is by no means the only one. There is going to be an increasing need for technicians and supervisors who can operate automated plants, and whose skills (unlike those of many traditional craftsmen) can be swiftly adapted to new methods and techniques. Draughtsmen are a continuing bottleneck in many sectors of industry.

Industry's replies to the 1970 Plan questionnaire indicated that demand for highly qualified manpower (scientists, technologists, technicians) is likely to grow four times as fast as the administrative, technical and clerical group as a whole. Demand for skilled operatives is forecast to grow half as fast again as total employment of manual workers. Particularly in demand will be qualified engineers (especially electrical and electronic and those concerned with production problems); mathematicians; chemists and physicists; work-study engineers; accountants and economists; computer operators and programmers; instrument mechanics, and electrical and electronic craftsmen.

At the other end of the scale, as we have seen, many traditional crafts are likely to disappear rather rapidly; while there is declining long-term demand, not only for routine clerical staff, unskilled labourers and production operatives, but also for certain types of machine-maintenance craftsmen. It is essential that all these changes should be foreseen and planned for.

The training boards thus have a critically important role to play in the modernization of Britain. Clearly they need to work closely with the Ministry of Technology and the Little Neddies. Like them, they are new bodies, feeling their way forward, and it will be some time before one can judge their effectiveness. Also, as in any attempt to apply general yardsticks to diverse industries, there will be hard cases. I know of some small engineering firms, for example, who are highly progressive concerns but who, for one reason or another, cannot qualify for training-board grants. But these are a small minority. On balance, the training boards can exercise a potent force for good in British industry – not least because, unlike the Little Neddies, they have the all-important power which comes from the authority to collect and dispense large sums of money.

## Planning for the Unplannable

It follows from all this, I believe, that if we are going to profit from technology we have got to plan ahead a great deal more thoroughly and more purposefully than we have done so far. Only by more thorough planning can we create the conditions in which the movement of resources can take place at the speed required, in the directions required, and without friction. The kind of planning we have been discussing in this book is not an alternative to competition; it is complementary to it.

Yet we have here a paradox; for, as we have seen, the forces of innovation are erratic and random in their movement, and where the lightning will strike cannot be foreseen in advance. We cannot, therefore, hope to pre-plan the advance of automation and technology fully. What we can do is to try so far as possible to remove the obstacles which a traditionally based society places in its path, and to cope with its consequences.

Let us take some examples. As automation develops, we may expect to see rapidly widening variations in productivity between the automated industries and the others. Automation is liable to be highly uneven in its incidence – both between industries and between different sectors of a single factory. As technology develops and living standards improve, we are likely to see a further shift in the balance of the labour force between manufacturing and the service trades at the inter-industry level, and between production and white-collar workers within a factory. If wages are based on productivity movements, we are likely to see some very sharp discrepancies developing. Many of the service trades, and many of the white-collar jobs in industry, cannot be automated; where their productivity is measurable, it is unlikely to show very big increases. If the full benefit of the increases in productivity brought about by automation is to go to those workers directly affected, therefore – and this will be a temptation in productivity bargaining – one of two consequences is liable to happen. On the one hand, the unautomated grades and industries could demand and secure comparable increases, despite the fact that their productivity had risen much more slowly, on the grounds of social justice and traditional differentials. This would be a recipe for perpetual wage inflation; for if the wage increases from automation were passed on to unautomated industries, their prices would be bound to rise. If, on the other hand, wage increases due to automation were restricted to one sector of the economy, the labour force would tend quickly to polarize into two groups with widely varying incomes and living standards. This new type of inequality – an inequality based on the varying pace of technology – could have serious social effects.

This does not mean that productivity bargaining is wrong or undesirable. It does, however, mean that it must take place within the framework of a national incomes and prices policy which seeks to share out the benefits of automation equitably throughout the community. In short, the onset of automation increases the urgency of achieving a viable long-term prices and incomes policy.

Changes in technology also require changes in the method of wage payment. In steel, for example, process workers have traditionally been paid on piece-rates, maintenance engineers on time-rates. The former, being the dominant group, have set the pace in wage negotiations, and the engineers have had to accept settlements based on prior agreements between management and process workers. But, as steel works have become more automated, the importance of the engineer *vis-à-vis* the process worker has steadily increased, and today the engineers insist that the wage structure should be built around them, and not the process worker. Such pressures increase the need for more scientific job evaluation procedures and more rational wage structures at plant level.

Second, what of the impact of automation on jobs? We have here a peculiarly difficult problem. As we have seen, the main labour problem which Britain is likely to face for the next decade, once expansion is resumed, will be one of shortage rather than of surplus. Yet the fear most people have of automation is that it will bring large-scale technological unemployment; and American experience, while inconclusive, tends to support this. At some stage, therefore, in the late seventies, Britain is quite likely to swing from a situation of crucial labour shortages to one of labour surplus, even if the economy is growing at a respectable rate. Indeed, if we were to improve the efficiency of our use of labour the change-over could come much more quickly – for, as we have seen, there has been a large element of artificiality in the shortage over the last few years.

We need desperately to plan ahead for this eventuality; and we need not only to plan, but to *be seen to be planning*, for only then will we be able to remove the fear of change from our people. If workers think that every introduction of automated techniques is going to bring unemployment or a drop in their living standards, they will resist it. They will not thus avoid unemployment, but they will succeed in slowing down the pace of change and therefore Britain's ability to compete in the world.

We have to plan ahead, therefore, for the eventuality of movements of manpower on a scale never before experienced in this country. Builders, printers, shipbuilders, car workers, mechanics, steelworkers, lift operators, many types of clerical workers, some grades of junior and middle management – all these are likely to be seriously affected by automation. Clearly we cannot, at this stage, sketch out with precision what are tomorrow's dead-end jobs – though it is clear that they include a substantial proportion of today's unskilled ones. One of the elements of uncertainty is that we do not yet know the limits to the tasks which computers can do, and therefore the extent of their likely invasion of the field of management. Clearly a wide range of routine clerical jobs will be replaced by computers in due course. But computers can do more than this. Even today it is possible to programme a computer to take logical decisions on things like stock control, buying policy, production schedules, quality control, prices and distribution networks a good deal faster and more reliably than humans can. This means that the old frontier between the realm of the machine and that of the human mind – the point at which decision-making begins – is no longer inviolable; and the implications for the future employment of middle management are somewhat uncomfortable. And as computers become increasingly sophisticated and advanced, the range of jobs they can do better than humans is going to become wider and wider.

Where major technological redundancies look like developing, it will be necessary for the public authorities to see what can be done to provide new industries in the same locality for the displaced workers to go to. The Steel Company of Wales, which has a serious over-manning problem, has been seeking to reduce its labour force at its Port Talbot works in South Wales, by agreement with the unions, by several thousand men. It would have found this very much easier if there were new factories available in the neighbourhood for the men to go to. Similar problems are going to confront many leading enterprises in the next few years. If new enterprises can be established to coincide with the labour run-down and to absorb it, the process of change is going to be achieved much more swiftly and smoothly, and the nation is going to be spared social dislocation and unrest, and the waste of labour resources. This is an important aspect of future regional planning.

Provided we can achieve the necessary mobility and the necessary provision of new skills, there should be no lack of new industries and jobs. Within industry we are going to need more technologists, technicians and supervisors; more managerial and white-collar workers in such fields as sales, research, training, welfare, personnel relations, systems analysis, process control, and so on. And there will be new industries to exploit the discoveries of technology. Clearly there will be a considerable expansion in the field of the science-based industries – computers, electronics, nucleonics, aerospace, automatic process-control equipment, telecommunications, and the like. Traditional technologies, such as energy or transport, are likely to be revolutionized and to spawn new industries – fuel cells, Hovertrack, etc. But many of the products and processes which will be earning the biggest profits in the late seventies do not exist at all today – except perhaps as a gleam in a scientist's eye. When we consider the importance in the national economy today of products and technologies which were literally not dreamed of forty, or thirty, or twenty years ago, it behoves us to go very warily about predicting the future.

And yet we cannot avoid doing so. In the public sector, particularly, we have to invest today to meet the presumed demands of thirty or forty years hence. In the fields of energy, transport and urban development particularly one has to look forward a quarter-century or more. Here at least there is no alternative to forward planning. The future cannot be commanded, but it must be prepared for.

Certain future needs we can, in any case, foresee. Among these are the needs of leisure, and the needs of knowledge. The satisfaction of these needs will provide the next decades with some of their biggest growth industries.

First, leisure. As living standards improve, it is to be expected that people will come to set a higher premium on leisure as opposed to money increases, and there will be a steady trend towards shorter working hours and longer holidays. There are already some indications that this is starting to happen in Britain, though the trend is less marked here than in most other advanced industrial countries. As automation progresses it will become increasingly important to bring down the average working week as an alternative to spreading technological unemployment. At the same time, the present vogue for long hours of overtime is not likely to prove a lasting phenomenon, once the artificially inflated labour shortage to which we have become accustomed disappears, and management starts to tackle productivity problems and wage structures more scientifically. In any case, people are increasingly, I believe, coming to realize that there is not much point in buying expensive consumer durables – motor cars, TV sets, record players, cine cameras and the like – if they have no time in which to enjoy them. In one or two industries, indeed, absenteeism has become a major problem for management.

Other factors, too, are going to increase the amount of leisure time at the community's disposal. It is probable that the average age of retirement will come steadily down as the century goes on. It is going to be more difficult to re-train older men, and this is likely to apply particularly to the business executive (as we saw in Chapter 4). The problems of readaptation would be reduced if earlier retirement came to be accepted as the norm. Housewives, too, are going to have more free time as the pattern of living becomes more automated and household drudgeries are steadily eliminated.

For the first time in history, in fact, the majority of the population is going to be able to lift its eyes from the perpetual problem of earning its daily bread, and to spend a substantial part of its time enjoying itself. To cater for this new trend there will need to be a great expansion in those service industries which are concerned with filling leisure time – entertainment, tourism, catering, and so on. Most of these industries are inevitably labour-intensive, offering little scope for automation. They are likely therefore to absorb a substantial part of the labour released from the automated industries.

The growth of leisure will itself, however, require a good deal of planning. More thought will need to be given to staggering holidays and working hours. The problem of accommodating the growing population of motor cars in our crowded island – particularly in our cities – will become more urgent than ever. Stricter controls may need to be exercised on motorists over wider areas than have been contemplated hitherto; and Buchanan-type projects for urban redevelopment will become a top priority. If shift working is to increase at the rate required, more social facilities will be needed in industrial communities to cope with the wants of those working late or awkward shifts – more all-night transport, shops and entertainments. It may well be, therefore, that the affluent society will have to accept more controls on its pattern of living, and a higher proportion of national income going in taxation, if the pattern of life is to be acceptable.

This is particularly true if the improvement in private living standards is to be accompanied by an improvement in the *quality* of living – and it will not be much use to us if it is not. The face of the future *could* be the Exeter by-pass on a summer bank holiday, or the smog-laden expressways of Los Angeles – but it must not. The first industrial revolution has left us an enormous legacy of ugly dereliction in the sprawling slums of the Black Country and the Pennine foothills. Today industry will not go to those areas if it can help it. Today the bait to attract new industries consists of good schools, shopping centres, technical institutes – even theatres, symphony orchestras and restaurants in the *Good Food Guide*. It will be even more so in the future. This is a sign both of spiritual and material progress. We have cut loose from the tyranny of more primitive technologies, which condemned industry to proximity to coal and smoke. What we now have to do is to clear up the mess our forefathers were compelled to leave. To do so will cost much public money. But it will provide work which may be needed, an outlet for our energies which will probably be needed, and an infrastructure for our children which will certainly be needed as a base for new industries, as well as an environment for healthier, happier living.

The problems of leisure will not, however, be solved simply by planning. Changes in psychology and social attitudes will also be needed, if affluence is to bring happiness and not discontent. Western Man – particularly in countries like Britain which have a puritan tradition – has been conditioned over the centuries to respect and indeed to reverence work, and to condemn, despise and fear idleness. But in the future an increasing number of us may have to accept idleness, in this sense, for a substantial part of our lives. If people are going to continue to act on the assumption that to be out of work confers a stigma of shame, and that the only end of life itself is work, they are going to be ill-adjusted to the coming Age of Leisure. Clearly we are going to have to go some way towards removing the traditional association of unemployment and poverty, by ensuring to those out of work a standard of living more nearly akin to salaries at work. But in doing this we must not go to the other extreme of removing all incentive to work, and of glorifying idleness.

Posterity will judge the men and women of the automation age by the use they make of their leisure. This could be mankind's golden age, the age in which the potential of the human spirit is brought to full flowering by the removal of the age-old burden of toil. Or it could be a period of boredom, neurosis, triviality and aimless violence. Human nature will be confronted with its greatest challenge – a challenge to its ingenuity, to its powers of adaptation, its character, creativeness and compassion, its ability to face change and make its institutions work in new and untried circumstances. Our ability to meet this challenge will depend in large measure on those spiritual reserves with which one believes – sometimes against all the evidence – that one's fellow men are endowed. But it will also depend to a considerable extent on the nature and quality of the education we give our people.

Of all the growth industries of the coming decades, the most important by far is going to be education. At every point its importance is apparent. We need to train far more people in the new skills of the automation age. We need to do far more to train workers for new jobs and to re-train those who have to give up their existing jobs. We must do more to educate our existing and potential business managers in the nature of their craft. We must bridge the gulf which at present exists between the arts man and the scientist, and between the theoretician and the practitioner of technology. We must find a new synthesis for the age of automation, and instil through our schools and places of education a greater understanding of the need for integration between the different sectors of our community. As the skill content of jobs increases, we have to make sure that the basic education of our people improves, so that we are not left – as America is in danger of being left – with a sub-class of unskilled who are below the threshold of employability in an era of rising standards of technology. And at the same time we have to teach people how to enjoy and appreciate leisure and to use it creatively. We have to teach people to live with themselves when the numbing injection of drudgery can no longer be administered to dull pain and pleasure alike. And this may be the hardest task of all.

All this is going to call for immense efforts, for new ideas and thinking, and for a much greater allocation of resources than we have been prepared to envisage hitherto. It is to be hoped that people will take a substantial part of the extra leisure they are going to get in the form of education. As technology advances, the premium on educational qualifications in the labour market is likely to increase. People will enter paid employment at a later age and leave it at an earlier one than they do today.

Both the United States and the Soviet Union are devoting more of their national resources to education – particularly to technical education – than we are. When I attended the British Industrial Exhibition at Moscow in 1962 the feature which impressed me, and many other of the exhibitors, was the high standard of general technical literacy among the average educated Russians. Lord Bowden, in an article in the *Listener* (22 October 1964), has described the 'obsession' which the Russians seem to have with 'the importance of mixing theory and practice'. It is a wise obsession; would we had it too! History will probably list, of all the achievements of the Russian Revolution – for good and ill – the most important and the most valuable as being the creation of mass literacy and mass numeracy: as the creation of the new class of educated Russians which is today beginning to take over and transform the society established by the Communist Party in Russia, and to strip it of the dogmas which have guided and nourished it hitherto. What we are now starting to witness in Russia, I believe, is a second revolution – a revolution founded on mass education. It will destroy traditional Communism just as surely as the Communists destroyed capitalism in Russia – but without bloodshed and suffering.

In planning for the automation age we cannot confine ourselves to these shores. The world is changing, under the pressures of technology, at a faster pace than ever before in history; that is one of the great clichés of our age, and like all such clichés it needs to be taken seriously. Hitherto, as we have seen, the great forcing-house of technology in the post-war era has been the needs of defence. It is to the cold war that we owe the enormous progress in aerospace and electronics, because only the threat of war could have called forth from the state the vast capital outpourings which these industries have needed. But we have now reached a moment in the history of the world at which it is legitimate to hope that the cold war as we have known it so far – that is, a clear confrontation between the Communist countries and the West – is in process of disappearing. New alignments are emerging, fraught it is true with equal or greater dangers for humanity. But the new conflicts are not likely to make the same demands on technology as the old; for it is precisely the *unevenness* of technological development which divides the new contestants.

We need, therefore, to consider seriously and soberly what we will do if Russia and America reach a *détente*. What will be done with the vast resources – particularly the technological resources – hitherto devoted to the arms race? No doubt a substantial proportion can be diverted with relatively little difficulty towards the acceleration of space technology; the inputs needed for the two endeavours overlap considerably in any event. There is also, as we have seen, a great deal of scope for achieving a broader spread of new technology in civilian industry. We can usefully spend much more money on training and education, and on modernizing the basic infrastructure of our society. There will be no lack of alternative outlets for the resources and energies liberated from the arms race. But the diversion will not take place of its own accord. Advance planning will be needed. And the publics of the Western democracies will need to be educated to the fact that it is as sensible for the state to spend money to improve the social structure and to modernize the economy as it is to spend money on defence; and that if high taxation is necessary for the latter, it may be necessary for the former too.

A considerable part of the resources freed from the cold war will need to go, also, in a greatly intensified campaign of aid and assistance to the underdeveloped and developing countries. Mankind will be no better off if the East–West conflict merely gives way to a North–South conflict, a permanent confrontation between the rich, white, industrialized nations (led by the United States, Russia and the European countries) and the poor, coloured agrarian lands of Asia, Africa and Latin America, with China at their head. Yet this is the danger that threatens us; and, if we are not careful, automation and the other new technologies are going to widen rather than narrow the gulf between the 'have' and the 'have-not' nations.

In the first place, automation is liable increasingly to offset the high labour costs of the richer countries, and so weaken one of the great assets the poorer countries at present enjoy. Second, the poorer countries cannot muster the capital resources and the 'know-how' needed for the application of the latest industrial techniques. As we have seen, as automation advances and the capital–labour ratio increases the threshold of employability rises; far too many of the workers of the poorer nations, through no fault of their own, fall below that threshold. Too many of the poorer countries lack the educational resources without which modern industrialization is almost impossible of achievement; and, when they do educate cadres of management, technicians and skilled men, these are liable to emigrate to the industrialized countries where life is easier and their skills assure them a welcome.

Moreover, the former dependence of the industrialized countries on commodity imports from the primary producers is diminishing, for two main reasons. First, the growth of plastics and other synthetic materials, and the greater interchangeability of materials and processes brought about by modern technology, are progressively liberating manufacturing industry from its former commodity base. Plastics can now be used in place of a wide range of metals, paper, timber and so on. Synthetic fibres compete with wool, cotton, silk and flax, synthetic rubber with natural rubber: the list could be extended almost indefinitely – and it is growing steadily longer. Second, the technological revolution is extending increasingly to agriculture. In Britain the rate of productivity increase in farming is among the highest for any major sector of activity. In Western Europe, as the peasant surplus continues to be absorbed in industry, agriculture is steadily becoming more capital-intensive and more highly productive. The grouping of farm holdings into larger units, as in the United Kingdom, is bound to accelerate this trend. The growing problem of world hunger is already reactivating the huge natural food surpluses of North America and the old 'white dominions' of the southern hemisphere, and reviving their traditional agricultural export trade.

In Britain today agriculture is already an enormously highly capitalized industry. With the development of 'factory farming' for livestock, the economies of large scale are bound to become increasingly important (as has been shown in the battery hen industry). The accelerated development of new fertilizers and pesticides is another factor leading to greatly enhanced food yields; this is likely to be particularly important for the Iron Curtain countries, whose agriculture has hitherto lagged sadly behind the targets set for it, but who are now undertaking a much belated investment in fertilizers on a massive scale. Looking a little further ahead, one can foresee a major eruption of new food technologies over the next decade or so in the advanced countries. Intensive cultivation in huge chemically treated fermentation vats; further rapid progress in freeze-drying and other forms of preservation of food; greater use of radiation techniques; scientific sea fish-farming; these and other developments which can be expected to materialize in the reasonably near future are going to increase the agricultural potential of the industrialized countries, and to make it progressively more difficult for peasant farmers to compete with the commercial farmer who is coming to dominate agriculture in the advanced industrial nations.

So the traditional advantages of the primary producing countries – cheap labour, access to raw materials, and in some cases natural power resources and/or good communications – are going to become less and less valuable to them as an offset to their disadvantages *vis-à-vis* the developed countries. (Even oil is likely to lose its attractions in an era of atomic energy and fuel cells!)

We cannot afford to allow the terms of trade and the divisions of wealth in the world to become further unbalanced; but that is what will happen if natural forces are allowed to take their toll. To counteract them, therefore, we need to do three things. First, we must step up the resources we devote to international aid and development, and we must plan their allocation much more intelligently and constructively, with more thought to the help they may give to the recipient and less to the incidental credit or benefit which might accrue to the donor. Second, we need to undertake urgent research into the types of simple or intermediate technology, not requiring high capital ratios, developed infrastructures or intensive technological 'know-how', which might be particularly appropriate for less-developed countries. Third, we have to plan for a new pattern of world trade, to replace the old one – whereby the less-developed countries traded food and raw materials for capital and manufactures – which no longer reflects existing comparative advantages or the current state of world technology. (Nor does it reflect the needs of humanity. In the Irish famine of the 1840s grain continued to be exported from Irish ports while the people starved. By the end of this century, on current trends, 300 million people in the less-developed countries will lack food. On current trends, again, that gap can only be filled by imports from the 'advanced' countries. An 'Irish' situation is unlikely to prove tolerable to the human conscience.)

The pattern of world trade which is likely to emerge is one in which the developed countries *export* temperate foodstuffs, capital and capital-intensive manufactures to the less developed, *importing* in exchange some tropical foodstuffs and raw materials, but to a growing extent manufactured goods embodying relatively simple technology and a relatively high labour content. There is a broad band of manufactures, particularly in the consumer goods field, which the advanced industrial countries ought not – according to strict comparative advantage – to be making; because they employ a high proportion of labour to capital, and that labour could be better employed elsewhere. Textiles and clothing, simple mechanical goods, bicycles, toys, cameras, furniture and furnishings, plastic fabrications, and so on, provide examples of the kind of industry which falls within this group. This does not mean that countries like Britain should forthwith cease all manufacture of furniture or wool textiles, for example. That would be ridiculous. What it *does* mean is that the less-developed countries should be encouraged to make more of these types of goods for export; and it follows that the industrialized countries should, as a group and as a deliberate act of policy, provide the freest possible entry for these imports into their home markets, and should undertake not to keep them out by tariffs or quotas. Britain has a better record than most of the other developed countries in this field – particularly in cotton textiles, which has been the most important test-case so far. But this policy can only work if the industrialized countries apply it collectively as a group. This will require the negotiation of periodic trade agreements – presumably through the U.N. Trade and Development Board (U.N.C.T.A.D.) – between the developed and the underdeveloped countries as a whole.

This is particularly important, since there is otherwise a danger of groups of underdeveloped countries attaching themselves to the peripheries of one or other of the big groups of developed countries – as France's former African territories have attached themselves, with the Turks and Greeks, to the European Economic Community. The danger is that this will distort the pattern of world trade, and prove seriously harmful to those underdeveloped countries that find themselves excluded (as Israel and Spain, for example, find themselves excluded from the natural pattern of Mediterranean trade by exclusion from the E.E.C. sphere of influence).

## Freedom, Knowledge and Necessity

This, then, is the prospect before us. This is the measure of our task and our opportunities. What are we going to do about it? The desirable changes which have been discussed in the pages above will not come about of their own accord. They will need to be consciously striven for, deliberately planned for. Without planning they will not, I believe, materialize. There is a real danger then that change will bring 'not peace, but a sword' – not happiness but misery, not wealth but unemployment and bitterness: a cruel betrayal of all our hopes. And if this were to happen – if, as happened in the years between the world wars, men and nations were to lose their capacity to control their economic destiny – who could foresee the consequences? Adam's children today have much bigger and more destructive toys to play with than Hitler ever enjoyed. Can we be sure they would not be used?

I believe, therefore, that we have to plan our future – both here in Britain and in the world at large; that we have to plan it with more care, more sophistication, more intelligence, more courage, and more humility, than we yet realize. At present in this country we are in a 'betwixt and between' stage. Government wishes to plan, but lacks the effective means to do so. The tools available lag far behind the aspirations. The efforts of the D.E.A., of the Ministry of Technology, Big Neddy and the Little Neddies, the Ministries of Labour, Public Building and the rest, which we have been discussing in this book, represent first faltering steps along the road we must take. We are like children who stumble when they try for the first time to walk. We fall over ourselves continually, and for most of the time we look extremely silly.

In these circumstances it is not surprising that we hear siren voices to left and right of us. The Left says: 'Be more ruthless. You cannot plan without strict controls. Enforce your will on the recalcitrants.' The Right says: 'Give it up. Planning is an illusion. Do not attempt to influence events, or to seek co-operation. Rely on the forces of the market, on the divine law of unlimited competition.' Both are wrong. We do not know enough about the future to pin our faith in controls, nor can we afford to dispense with the forces of competition. But neither can we seek to grapple with the technology of today by blind adherence to an economic theory based on that of two centuries ago. Those who pin their faith on the dogmas of Adam Smith betray a naïve and touching innocence about the nature of the world of today, rather like those charming childhood pictures of Chagall, complete with winged priests and strange mythical beasts. It is not dogma that we need, whether it be the dogma of Left or Right, but knowledge.

To plan properly we need one thing above all: we need more, vastly more, information. The state needs to have at its disposal the same range of information, in the same detail, as the individual firm uses for its own forward planning. No business-man today conducts his organization without some element of forward planning, based on the best knowledge available about his business operations and his market, and a control mechanism. There should be no difficulty in principle about the government obtaining from the individual industries and firms (with due regard for confidentiality) the same information. Nor, with the range of computers now available, is there any insuperable obstacle to the effective collection and evaluation of this in-formation. All that is required is for each enterprise to provide government, on a regular basis, with the kind of basic statistical information which the chief executive regularly receives and on which he normally bases his decisions. In this way the govern-ment would have, what it now lacks, a complete profile of the economy, an indication of the trend of orders and the pressure on resources in each sector, a guide to the sensitive points and the areas where intervention of some form or other is required. This information would be fed into computers, which would be programmed to flash warning signals when, in any sector, the economy was diverging from the planned path, with an indication of the remedial action required.[6] (This does not mean, of course, that the behaviour of the economy must always be adjusted to the Plan. Often it will be the other way round. The information fed in will enable the errors of the Plan to be more quickly recognized, so that it will become a more flexible and realistic instrument.) There is nothing revolutionary about this concept. It merely represents the application at national level of the kind of techniques increasingly employed by the more up-to-date business enterprises. Of course the operation would be a complex one to mount (though, once mounted, not particularly difficult to sustain). But it strikes me as more rational, and more likely to give the right answers, than a mystical 'hidden hand' which works in unspecified ways, or the only too material hand of a gentleman in Whitehall imposing major decisions on a basis of hunch and totally inadequate information. We have criticized the attitude of amateur management in industry, and its day is happily passing. But in the current state of planning in this country the management of the economy as a whole is still very much at the amateur stage.

We have to build, then, on the foundations which we are now starting to lay, an edifice of voluntary planning, based on complete information and cooperation, and using the full resources which modern technology can provide, which will enable the national economy to be steered as a large business enterprise is steered today. And, eventually, this type of planning must be extended to the international scene. The need is too urgent, the opportunities too great, to be deterred by considerations of mystique or dogma. The greater the pace of change, the more swift and unpredictable the impulses of innovation, the greater is the need for knowledge, the more vital the necessity for cooperation and partnership between the various sectors of the community. As Spinoza, quoting St John the Divine, said: 'You shall know the Truth, and the Truth shall make you free' – even if, as he believed, freedom is only the knowledge of necessity. The genie is out of Aladdin's lamp now. We can never put him in again. But can we find the words which will make him our slave, and not our master?

NOTES TO CHAPTER SEVEN

1. For a fuller discussion of these matters, see my *The Stagnant Society* (Penguin Books, 1961).

2. See 'Britain's Biggest Scandal: How Men are Wasted', by Anthony Bambridge, *Observer*, 8 August 1965.

3. op. cit.

4. See Chapter 1 (page 35).

5. See *The Stagnant Society* (p. 150).

6. See the Fabian Society pamphlet, *The New Economy*, by Jeremy Bray, M.P. (July 1965).

# POSTSCRIPT

WHILE this book was being printed, the Prime Minister's National Productivity Conference on 14 June 1967 considered as one of its main items a paper on the role of technology in productivity. The main theme of the paper was that Britain, despite her large R. & D. effort, has been getting less in terms of economic growth from technological progress than her competitors in Western Europe; and it set out, as this book has set out, to find the reasons.

Comparatively low rates of capital investment are, the paper argued, only part of the reason for our relatively poor performance. At least equally important has been our failure to use existing capital to best advantage. There is a reluctance in many cases to scrap old plant quickly enough. Too much expensive plant is under-utilized, for example through failure or inability to organize double-shift or three-shift working. Too many of our scientists and engineers are engaged on R. & D. work, and not enough in other activities such as production, technical selling and general management. Some redeployment of our resources in this field as between industry, government establishments and universities should lead to a quicker and more effective diffusion of technology in industry.

The paper went on to pinpoint some of the areas offering the greatest scope for technological application. 'The immediate need', it said, 'is for a rapid increase in the use of known technologies.' A greater design effort in the field of automatic assembly and numerical control of machine tools, together with greater emphasis on variety control and Value Analysis, is one example. There is considerable scope for more low-cost and process automation. In the field of mechanical handling, packaging, storage and distribution the opportunities for wider application of modern techniques is substantial. But if these opportunities are to be realized there must be a more sustained and concentrated drive to disseminate information on new techniques, products and processes throughout industry, and to raise the standards of technical and commercial awareness among the managers who will have to apply them. And more thought may need to be given to ways of getting companies over the threshold of technological application, by overcoming the uncertainties and hesitations which afflict many managements when contemplating innovation.

Ways of doing this include, for example:

1. 'Buy-or-return' schemes, such as the N.R.D.C. already operates for numerically controlled machine tools, under which users can purchase advanced equipment with the option of returning it within two years, in return for a small premium and a fixed monthly charge for the period for which the equipment has been used.

2. Pre-production orders, as currently in use for machine tools. Under this scheme the Government buys the equipment and makes it available to selected users for economic and technical appraisal under industrial conditions. This helps to shorten the lead-time between development and full commercial application of the equipment.

3. Advisory and demonstration centres (now being developed for numerically controlled machine tools) to make industry familiar with the use and advantages of advanced equipment.

4. The provision of training, advisory and consultancy services based on technical colleges where firms could develop ideas using commercial equipment in, e.g., the field of low-cost automation.

5. 'Joint-venture' pioneering schemes to develop new systems, on the basis of a three-way partnership between university teams (or government laboratories), process control companies and manufacturers.

The paper concluded by suggesting a number of experiments 'aimed at discovering the techniques most useful to particular sectors of industry, studying the reasons why they have not been used, and identifying the means to encourage their application.' These experiments could be a joint endeavour between government and industry and could be on the basis of a particular product, an industry, or a geographical location. Thus one would analyse the reasons why some new products succeeded and others did not; why some industries were successful innovators and others not; why some areas have a better record for industrial creativity than others.

Such case studies would be difficult to mount effectively, and perhaps equally difficult to sell to some of the participants. (As we have seen, the reasons for technological lag can go very deep indeed.) But if these obstacles could be overcome, and the necessary resources for a full-scale technical audit deployed, we might at the end of the day be a lot nearer to knowing the answers to the intricate and complex questions which this book has been concerned to explore. With this renewed plea for more knowledge, therefore, this book may appropriately end.

While this book was going to press, it was announced that English Electric had made a bid for Elliott-Automation. If this goes through, it will lead to a considerable rationalization of the computer industry, as advocated in Chapter 5. However, in my view it will still probably be desirable in the long term to merge I.C.T. and English Electric to create a unified national computer industry.

# APPENDIX

Syllabus for M.Sc. Students at London Graduate School of Business Studies, 1967

QUANTITATIVE METHODS AND ANALYSIS

*M 101 Accounting I*
Concepts and aims. Operating and income accounts. Balance sheets. Auditing procedures. Accounts of non-manufacturing business. Limitations of statutory accounts. Financial ratios. The valuation of a business.

*M 102 Accounting II*
Management accounting. Planning, budgeting and control. Cost analysis. Assessment of profitability and performance. Inter-firm comparisons. Organization for financial control. Data processing for accounting systems.

*M 103 Economic Analysis for Business Decisions*
Optimization and marginal analysis. Demand analysis and measurement. Cost concepts and analysis. Theory of production. Pricing. Product evaluation and resource allocation. Market concepts and market structures. Economic aspects of organization. Corporate strategy and objectives. Capital budgeting.

*M 104 Mathematics I*
Logic and set theory. Elementary algebra; the binomial theorem. Sequences and limits. Differential calculus; maxima and minima. Lagrange multipliers. Taylor's theorem. Elementary functions.

*M 105 Mathematics II*
Elementary integral calculus. Mean value theorem. Vectors and matrices; input–output tables. Matrix operations; determinants, inversions. Linear transformations. Properties of matrices and transformations. Difference and differential equations.

## M 106 *Mathematics III*
Algorithms for solution and optimization. Introduction to computers. Flow charts. Computer programming. Description and transformation of systems. Markov chains.

## M 107 *Statistics I*
The meaning of probability. Expected values and utility. Random variables and probability distributions. Opportunity losses. Statistical decision rules with binomial or normal sampling. Economics of two-action problems. Optimal sample sizes.

## M 108 *Statistics II*
Testing hypotheses. Point and internal estimation. Confidence limits. Analysis of frequencies. Simple non-parametric tests. Simple problems of regression and association. Multiple regression. Analysis of variance and experimental design. Principles of sample surveys. Quality control schemes.

## M 109 *Introduction to Logic and Scientific Method*
Syllabus under review

## M 201 *Operations Research I*
Nature of Operations Research. Formulation of problems. Construction of models. Mathematical programming, including linear and dynamic. Applications of programming to various problem areas such as production, marketing, pricing and investment. Econometric analysis. Inter-industry analyses. Economic decision-making under uncertainty.

## M 202 *Operations Research II*
Inventory and production control. Simulation and Monte Carlo methods. Queueing and sequencing models. Replacement and renewal models. Simple game theory and optimal strategies. Network analysis. Systems analysis for computer applications. Problems of organization and implementation.

ENVIRONMENTAL STUDIES

## M 110 *Macroeconomics I*
National income accounting. The determination of national income. Business fluctuations. Banking and the structure of the capital market. Rates of interest. Policies for control and stabilization.

## M 203 *Macroeconomics II*
Contemporary problems of inflation, growth and balance of payments. National economic planning.

## M 111 *International Trade and Development*
The basis of trade. Determinants of trade flows. Balance of payments adjustments. Commercial policies. International finance and institutions. Problems of developing areas.

## M 112 *Industrial and Business Structure I*
Industrial structure, size-distribution, location and structure of firms and plants, and the determinants of changeover time. Firm structure; sources of authority, the divorce of ownership and control. Contemporary industrial control structures.

## M 204 *Industrial and Business Structure II*
The role of government as a consumer, supplier and investor. Investment criteria for government agencies. The social control of industry. Nationalized industries and the promotion of industrial activities. The control of monopoly and restrictive practices.

## M 205 *Managerial Dynamics*
The growth of the modern corporation. The role of economic and social forces in shaping corporate development. The analysis of technical change and productivity growth. Entrepreneurship and innovation. The diffusion process. The implementation of change. Research and change.

## M 113 *Corporate Legal Environment*

Legal aspects of incorporation. Legal aspects of company financial structure. The rights and powers of shareholders and directors. Legal principles of taxation. Principles of contract law, the sale of goods and patents. Contracts of employment. The legal status of trade unions.

### FUNCTIONAL STUDIES

## M 206 *Finance I*

Basic concepts of profitability, risk and uncertainty in relation to investment. Management of assets. Capital budgeting under uncertainty. The incidence of taxation. Replacement decisions.

## M 207 *Finance II*

Concepts of the cost of capital. The choice of finance. The new issue market. Institutional lenders. Leasing. Capital gearing and the cost of capital. Taxation and company policies. Take-overs. Long-term financial planning.

## M 208 *Production*

Method study and work study techniques. Ergonomic principles. Work design. Product design and development. Basic manufacturing processes. Evaluation of alternate materials and processes. Variety control. Production planning, scheduling and time-tabling. Production and inventory control. Purchasing. Total quality control. Maintenance. Measuring production performance.

## M 209 *Marketing I*

The nature and scope of marketing decisions and the data and concepts useful in making them. Market analysis. Product formulation to meet consumer needs. Pricing. Distribution channels and policies. Competitive strategies. Organization for marketing. Financial projection, control and evaluation in marketing. Integration with other business areas and with general company policies. Special factors in international marketing.

## M 210 *Marketing II*

Tactical aspects of product and marketing management. The build-up of the product line and problems of product deletion. Decisions on branding, packaging, container and label design. Building and reviewing marketing programmes. The characteristics and uses of the different marketing tools available: advertising, personal selling, external distribution channels, sales promotions, price promotions. Measuring the effectiveness of specific marketing actions.

### BEHAVIOURAL STUDIES

## M 114 *Human Behaviour*

A survey of some basic concepts of individual and group behaviour. Topics covered include: individuality, perception, socialization, attitudes, motivation, learning, group dynamics, influence role and social stratification. Application to economic and administrative behaviour.

## M 115 *Organizational Behaviour*

The behaviour of individuals and groups in organizations with particular emphasis on organizational processes. Topics include: structures and functions, communication, leadership, innovation, diffusion and organizational change. Application specially directed toward administrative policies that significantly affect the behaviour of the organization's human resources.

## M 211 *The Individual and the Organization*

Sources and effects of personal executive conflict inside the firm and the functional and dysfunctional consequences of this conflict. The course examines the following selected problem areas: management ideologies, occupational succession, career mobility and executive roles, the psychodynamics of insubordinacy and post-decisional conflict.

## M 212 *Personnel Management and Industrial Relations*

Problems of personnel selection and training. Selection

techniques. Personnel development. Labour relations. Compensation systems. Productivity agreements. Collective bargaining. Labour disputes. Industrial relations and government. Work-force organization.

## INTEGRATIVE STUDIES

*M 213 and M 214 Business Policy and Organization*
The application of the disciplinary and functional studies in an integrated approach to general management problems. These include the setting of objectives, strategy and policies, the organization of the company appropriate to its objectives, the planning of effective relations with a work force, the design of overall company systems of planning and control; licensing, joint ventures and mergers.

# INDEX

# INDEX

Absenteeism, 258

Administrative Staff College, 210

Advertising, 32

Advisory Council on Science and Technology, 157

Advisory Council on Technological Policy, 154

Aerospace industries, 45, 80–81, 154, 175–6

Agriculture, 264–5

Allen, William W., 34–7, 242

American Telephone and Telegraph Company, 94

Annan Impey Morrish, 203

Anti-trust legislation, U.S., 82

Ashridge College, 210–11

Associated Electrical Industries, 166, 172

Associated Industrial Consultants, 52, 203, 205

Aston University Small Business Centre, 215

Atomic Energy Authority, 153, 156, 161, 173

Automatic process control, 40, 51

Automation, 37–42, 216
  cybernetics in, 51
  labour and, 239–57
  underdeveloped countries and, 264
  union opposition to, 53
  U.S.A., in, 52, 74, 77–8
  wage increases and, 253–5
  working week and, 258

Automation-equipment industry, 142, 166–8, 170–71

Austria, 15–16, 40

Balance of payments, 23, 27, 102–3

Banwell Report 1964, 228–9

Battelle Memorial Institute, 47

Beeching, Dr, 209

Beer, Stafford, 71

Belgium, 39

Bell organization, 94

Benn, Anthony Wedgwood, 106

Binder Hamlyn Fry & Co., 203

Board of Trade, 110–11, 136–7, 151–3, 179–80

Booz-Allen, 205

Boston, Mass., 142–3

Bowden, Lord, 262

Brain drain, 44, 196–7

Brisch, E. G., 205

British Institute of Management, 131, 212, 215

British Motor Corporation, 135, 242

British Overseas Airways Corporation, 246–7

British Productivity Council, 187, 213, 215

British Railways, 42

Brown Boveri Ltd, 164

Brown, George, 29, 106, 112

Building, 59–60, 78–9, 83, 99, 222–31

Business,
  games, 53, 207
  Operations Research, 204
  orientation in U.S.A., 92–3
  schools, 145, 207, 209–12

Cambridge, 53
Capacity utilization rate, 19, 36
Capital investment, 20, 22, 53, 273
Centre for Interfirm Comparisons, 131, 215
Chemical research, 79–80
Civil Service, 106–8, 183
Cold war, 263
Colvilles, 135–6
Committee of Enquiry into the Organization of Civil Science, report of, 152
Communism, education and, 262–3
Companies Act 1966, 131
Computer-controlled lending library, 199
Computer industry,
  Britain, in, 153–4, 164, 167–70, 172–3
  location of, 142
  operational research, in, 51
  U.S. dominance of, 164–6
Computer installation, international comparison of, 39, 40, 169
Computer techniques in management training, 69
Computer-typesetting, 217
Computers,
  effect on manpower, 256
  management, in, 97, 101n.
  underemployed in Britain, 252
Concord project, 175, 177

Confederation of British Industry, 149, 184–5, 187
Conservative Government, 110, 137, 190, 227, 250
Consumer saturation, 16, 34
Contract research, 47–50, 91–2, 201–2
Cooper Brothers, 203
Courtaulds Ltd., 209
Cousins, Frank, 106
Cranfield Aeronautics College, 211
Critical path analysis, 57, 59
Cryogenics, 81
Cybernetics, 51, 71

Data processing, electronic, 42, 170
Decca, 166
Decentralization, 137, 147–8
Decision theory, 54
Decision-Tree concept, 54, 56, 60
Defence,
  civil technology and, 158, 160
  network analysis in, 55
  operational research in, 50, 53
  P.E.R.T. charts and, 57
  procurement agencies, 147
  research, 45, 80, 156–7
  systems planning in, 84
  technology, 174
Deflation, 102–4
Department of Economic Affairs, 105–6, 108, 111–12, 149, 180, 186
  Central Planning Unity, 138
  economic growth and, 111
  Industrial Division, 125–6
  Regional Policy Division, 136

Department of Education and Science, 152, 213

Department of Scientific and Industrial Research (D.S.I.R.), 82, 151-3

Development areas, 31, 136, 139, 140-49

Desalination, 161

Diebold, John, 205

Discounted cash flow technique, 118-19

Distribution rationalization, 52-3

Du Pont, 57, 67, 242

East Kilbride, 145

Economic development committees, 127-31, 149, 180, 184-6

Economist Intelligence Unit, 205

Edinburgh, 147

Education, 75, 77, 107, 139, 261-2

Efficiency, need for, in Britain, 23, 104, 111, 120, 186

Elections, incomes policy and, 28

Electricity Council, 36

Electronics industries, 142, 153-5, 163-6

Elliott-Automation, 160, 166, 169-72

Emerson, 201, 242

Engineering industry, 119, 122, 154-5

Engineering Training Board, 250-51

English Electric, 166-7, 170, 172

Esso, 35-6

Europe, economic growth in, 15-17

European Defence Community, 174

European Economic Community, 39, 267

Britain's bid to enter, 133, 177

European Free Trade Association, 40

European joint development projects, 173-7

European technological community, conditions for, 177-8

Export-import balance, 128, 130, 156

Fawley productivity agreements, 35-6, 53

Ferranti Ltd, 147, 166, 172

*Financial Times, The*, 58, 189

Flow process chart, 55

Flowers Committee, 169

Food industry, 265

Forster, E. M., 89

France, 15, 24, 34, 39, 44-5, 82, 99, 132, 148, 164, 166, 214, 224, 226-7, 245

British cooperation with, 173-6

Franks, Lord, 69, 210

Freeman, C., 44

Full employment, 25, 36, 133

Fulton Committee on Civil Service, 108, 182

Games theory, 53

Gantt chart, 55

Geddes report on shipbuilding, 208

Germany, West, 15-16, 34, 39, 41, 44, 82, 176, 232, 245

Government,
  Housing Corporation, 249
  industrial advisers in, 126-7

Government – *continued*
  intervention, 18–19, 106
  machinery,
    efficiency probe into, 181–2
    expertise in, 183
  Office of Scientific and Technical information, 199
  policy, instability of, 22–3, 26
  relations with industry, 105–8, 127, 149–50, 179–80, 187, 189
  role in economic growth, 98–190
  role in innovation, 98–101
Grenoble, 148
Group dynamics, 67, 207
Growth centres, technological, 141–7
'Growth, dash for', theory, 22
Growth, economic, 24–5, 30–33
  British, 19–20, 25–6
  capital investment and, 116–17
  efficiency and, 104–5
  international comparisons of, 16, 192–3
  technological training key to, 143
  U.S.A., in, 16
  U.S. methods needed for, 38–9

Harvard Business School, 69–70, 197, 211
Heyworth, Lord, 50, 54
H.M.S.O., 189
House of Commons, 183
Houston, Texas, 142–3

Illinois Institute of Technology, 47

Imperial Chemical Industries, 36, 209, 236, 242, 244
Imports surcharge, 103
Incentive payments schemes, 206
Income, increases in national, 16
Incomes policy, *see* Prices and incomes policy
Industrial advisers, 126–7
Industrial Reorganization Corporation (I.R.C.), 123, 159, 170, 172–3
Industrial Training Act 1964, 250
Industry,
  assessment of standards in, 131–2
  centralization of authority in, 184
  changes in British, 24
  large and small firms in, 214–22
Inflation, 18–19, 75, 77, 102, 104
Information dissemination, 86, 90–92, 99, 151
Information retrieval, 80–81, 198–9
Information scientist, 90
Innovation, 33, 46, 63–7, 191, 233
  centralization and, 186
  effect on underdeveloped countries, 264–6
  European strategy needed for, 178
  failure rate in, 232
  impact on labour, 239–57
  main obstacles to, 191–237, 253
  management of, 231–7, 274
  national strategy for, 158–9, 168, 171

public procurement and, 132,
   160
tax incentives for, 160
International Business Machines
   (I.B.M.), 165, 167–9, 171
International Computers and
   Tabulators (I.C.T.), 160,
   167–71, 251
International Publishing Cor-
   poration, 36
Inventory control, 52–3
Investment, *see also* Capital
   analyst, 46
   appraisal techniques, 84–5,
      117–19, 189
   control, 103
   European comparisons of,
      192–3
   incentives, 116–17
   planning, 27, 120
   returns, 192–3
Ireland, Northern, 135, 137, 227
Israel, 144, 267
Italy, 15, 34, 39, 82, 214, 245

Japan, 15–16, 33, 165–6, 214,
   232, 245
Johnson, President, 77, 82
Joint Electronics Scheme, 147


Kennedy, President, 87, 99


Labour,
   automation's impact on, 239–57
   costs,
      international comparisons of,
         38
      U.S.A., in, 16, 43
   demand for, 31–2, 139, 252,
      257

force, statistics of, 244–5
Government, 18–19, 32, 38,
   102–4, 223
mobility, 31, 78, 124, 134–5,
   239, 242, 248–9, 256
Party, 100, 149
productivity, 33, 35, 39, 114,
   123–4, 244–5
run-down, 242–8, 256–7
shortage, 34, 37–8, 104, 244–5,
   255
surplus, 21, 32–4, 255
training, 249–53
underemployment,       242–3,
   246–7
*Laisser faire*, 110
Leisure, age of, 258–61
Line of balance technique, 55
*Listener, The*, 262
Little, Arthur D., 47–50, 52, 54,
   142, 201
Living standards, 16–17
*Lloyds Bank Review*, 17
Local government reform, 138,
   227
Location of industry, 53, 135,
   141–5
Lockouts, 248
London Business School, 69,
   276–81


Machines Bull, 165
Machine tools, 79, 122, 129, 153,
   155
McKinsey & Co., 181, 201–3, 205
MacNamara, R. S., 84, 99
Maddison, Angus, 17
Magee, John, 54
Management,
   branch, 139–40

Management – *continued*
  computer impact on, 96–7, 101
  consultants, 95, 181–2, 200–206
  corporate planning and, 188
  expertise in, 194–6, 198
  failures in Britain, 121
  innovations of, 231–7
  mobility, 91–3, 96, 200, 208–9
  new demands on, 66–8, 71
  research relationships with, 62–7, 68, 90, 93
  salary structure, 197–8
  selection, 204, 208–9
  services for small firms, 214
  techniques, 43, 54–5, 69, 81, 206–7
  training, 68–70, 91, 200, 207, 209–13
Managers, useful life of, 96
Manchester University, 146
Marconi, 166, 172
Market research, 24, 53, 236
Marketing policy, 122
Marketing techniques in U.S.A., 43, 50
Martel guided missile, 175
Massachusetts Institute of Technology (M.I.T.), 48, 70, 84, 142–3, 145–6, 233
Maud Committee, 138
Maudling, Reginald, 26, 28, 112
Mechanical Engineering Economic Development Committee, 122–3, 129, 160
Mechanization, advanced, 42
Metra-Sigam-Martech, 204, 206
Micro-circuits, 170, 172–3
Miniaturization, 81, 178
Ministry for Science, 149–50, 152

Ministry of Aviation, 153, 156
Ministry of Housing, 226, 229
Ministry of Industry, case for, 179–81
Ministry of Labour, 213, 241, 248, 250
Ministry of Public Building and Works, 59, 226
Ministry of Technology, 82, 105–6, 111, 147
  Industrial Liaison Service, 155, 215
  organization, 154–6
  origin, 149–53
  payroll, 161–2
  problems facing, 157–69, 233
  Research Group, 155–6
  role, 153–4
  successor, 179–81
Mullard, 172

National Agricultural Advisory Service, 215
National Board for Prices and Incomes (N.B.P.I.), 113, 115, 185, 220–21, 242
National Building Agency, 226
National Coal Board, 241
National Computer Centre, 169
National Economic Development Council (N.E.D.C.), 15, 23–31, 33, 152
  growth target of, 36–7
  planning function of, 128, 151
  publications, 25, 112, 117–19
National Electronics Research Council, 199
National Engineering Laboratory, 153, 161
*National Institute Economic Review*, 165, 171

National Physical Laboratory, 153, 161

National Research Development Corporation (N.R.D.C.), 82, 151–3, 156, 160–61, 171, 173

Netherlands, 39

Network analysis, 55–62, 81, 84

North Atlantic Treaty Organization, 174

Nucleonic industries, 142, 173, 178

Numerical control, 40, 42, 74, 161, 167

Oil companies, 36

Olivetti, 164

Operational research, 50–55, 71, 89

Organization for Economic Co-operation and Development, 44

Overtime, 125, 243, 245–6, 258

Paish, Prof. Frank, 21

Paishian economic school, 21–2, 76, 104

Palo Alto, Cal., 142, 144

P.A. Management Consultants, 203

Pask, Gordon, 51

Payroll tax, 114

Peat Marwick Mitchell, 203

Pension transferability, 249

Philips, 164

Plan, National, 1970, 103–4, 111, 187, 222, 228, 231, 252

Planning, 137, 185–6
    corporate, 62, 87, 188, 208, 213
    forward, 257, 259–60, 263
    local authorities', 53, 227

manpower, 243, 247, 255
    national, 23–4, 53, 98, 120, 126, 130, 140, 186–8, 268–71
    regional, 137–8, 257

Plessey Co. Ltd, 172

Plowden Report, 175

Political and Economic Planning (P.E.P.), 151–2

Portugal, 40

Post Office, 52, 128, 169, 171, 181, 202

Poverty, 16, 32–3, 77, 89

Pressed Steel, 36

Price control, 29, 186

Prices and incomes policy, 15, 27–31, 112–15, 132, 184, 186, 254

Price Waterhouse & Co., 203

Printing, 216–22, 237

Process Plant Working Party, 123

Production control, 208

Production Engineering Research Association (P.E.R.A.), 155, 203, 215

Production planning, 27, 53

Productivity,
    agreements, 35–6, 115–16, 243–4, 246, 254
    Conference 1967, 273–5
    lag in Britain, 17–19, 35–7
    promoted by price control, 115
    rise in Britain, 41, 104, 244, 264
    rise in U.S.A., 37, 73–4, 76–7

Programme evaluation and research technique (P.E.R.T.), 57, 59, 66

Protectionism, 121, 168, 170, 177–9

Public procurement, 132, 160, 169, 172, 176, 178

Qualitative product screening, 235

Queueing theory, 52, 55

Radar, 165–6

Radio, 165–6

Rand Corporation, 48

Rationalization in industry, 120, 123, 129, 132, 170, 172–3, 185

Rawle, L. J., 60–61

Regional development policy, 133–49

Regional devolution, 137–8

Regional employment premiums, 31

Remington Rand, Ltd, 57

Resale price maintenance, 185

Research, 64–5, 79–80
    application, 145, 165–6, 174, 232, 273
    associations, 82, 92, 147, 151, 153, 156, 161, 232–3
    coordination, 157–8, 161
    councils, 152
    expenditure, 44–6, 156–7
    management relationships with, 62–7, 68, 90, 93

Research and Development,
    Britain, in, 46–7, 169, 232–7, 273
    contracts, 169
    decentralization, 148
    engineer–scientist ratios in, 45
    government-industry coopera-
      tion in, 149–50, 162–4
    government investment in, 79–80, 150–52
    international specialization in, 178

investment returns, 63–5, 157, 273
    U.S.A., in, 43, 45, 47, 86

Resource allocation,
    multi-project scheduling, and, 57
    operational research and, 53

Restrictive practices, 35, 124–5, 190, 220

Restrictive Trade Practices Act, 121

Retirement age, 258

Richard Thomas & Baldwin Ltd, 235

Robson Morrow & Co., 203    ,

Rootes Ltd, 135

Science-based industries, 141–4, 257

Scientific Instrument Manufac-
    turers Association, 163–4

Scientific revolution, 62

Scotland, 135–8, 145–7

Selective Employment Tax, 115, 134, 189

Semi-conductor industry, 94

Serendipity, 66, 72

Sheffield University, 171

Shift-working, 259

Shipbuilding, 154–5, 208

Siemens, 164, 166

Social infrastructure, 32, 140, 259–60

Spain, 267

Standardization, 120–21, 123, 219, 225, 227–8

Stanford Research Institute, 47, 188, 202

Steel Company of Wales, 36, 256

Sterling crises, 22, 104

Stewart, Michael, 106

Stewarts & Lloyds Ltd, 242

Stock control, 52, 208

'Stop–go' policy, 18–21, 38, 103–4, 120, 223, 244

Strathclyde University, 145

Strikes, unofficial, 248

Sub-contracting, 60, 119, 122

*Sunday Times*, 34

Sussex University, 171

Sweden, 225, 239, 242, 249

Switzerland, 39

Systems analysis, 78, 251–2

Systems engineering, 81, 84, 93–8

Taxation, 197

Teaching aids industry, 171, 206–7

Technical audit, 63, 67

Technology, diffusion of, 78–89, 107, 156, 230, 232, 273–4

Telecommunications, 153–4, 165, 171, 173, 178

Telefunken, 164

Textiles, 79, 209

Thomson, Lord, 217

Toothill, Sir John, 40, 147

Trade associations, 130, 184–5

Trade unions, 185, 239–40

bargaining powers, 19, 22, 30–31, 53, 247–8

incomes policy and, 27–31

innovation and, 239–41, 246–7

restrictive practices, 124–5, 190, 220–21, 227–8, 242, 247

U.S., 239

Trades Union Congress, 184, 187, 240

Transport, 52, 94–5

Treasury, 25, 109, 111

Trend, Sir Burke, 152

Underdeveloped countries, 32, 263–7

Unemployment, 21, 32

automation and, 73–8

Britain, in, 134–5, 255

U.S.A., in, 37–8, 75–7, 99

Unilever Ltd, 60–61

United States of America,

Administration, 81, 84–5, 87–9, 99, 100

Air Force, 52, 84

Army Ordnance Bureau, 55

Defence Department, 84

Department of Labor, 75–6, 249–50

Institute of Applied Technology, 85

National Aeronautics and Space Administration, 80

National Commission on Technology, Automation and Economic Progress, 77

Navy, 57

State Technical Service Act, 85–6

University, industry and, 146–7

University research laboratories, 47–8

Urwick Orr & Partners Ltd, 203, 205

U.S.S.R., 40, 44–5, 62, 99, 100, 148, 224, 262–4

Value analysis, 207, 273

Variety control, 120–21, 132, 161, 168, 208, 216, 273

Vietnam war, 74, 77

Volkswagen, 242

Wage

drift, 22, 30–31

Wage – *cont.*
  freeze, 31, 113
  inflation, 30–31, 34, 253–5
  levels, forces determining, 30–
    31
  -price spiral, 19, 3
Wales, 137
Weizmann Institute, 144
Wilson, Harold, 39, 62
Work Study, 208

World trade, 266–7

Xerox, 171

Young, A., 44
Youngstown Sheet and Tube,
  242

Zuckerman, Sir Solly, 157

## MORE ABOUT PENGUINS
## AND PELICANS

*Penguin Book News*, an attractively illustrated magazine which appears every month, contains details of all the new books issued by Penguins as they are published. Every four months it is supplemented by *Penguins in Print*, which is a complete list of all books published by Penguins which are still available. (There are well over two thousand of these.)

A specimen copy of *Penguin Book News* can be sent to you free on request, and you can become a regular subscriber at 3s for twelve issues (with the complete lists). Just write to Dept EP, Penguin Books Ltd, Harmondsworth, Middlesex, enclosing a cheque or postal order, and your name will be added to the mailing list.

Some other books published by Penguins are described on the following pages.

Note: *Penguin Book News* and *Penguins in Print* are not available in the U.S.A., Canada or Australia.

# PENGUIN TECHNOLOGY SURVEY 1967
### EDITED BY ARTHUR GARRATT

*Creative Engineering*

## THE NEW ENGINEER
### R. A. SMITH
## RECENT TECHNOLOGICAL ADVANCES IN JAPAN
### KANKURO KANESHIGE

*Engineering Materials*

## THE DEVELOPMENT OF WATER RESOURCES
### PETER C. G. ISAAC
## TECHNOLOGY OF PLASTICS
### NORMAN DENTON

*Automation*

## AUTOMATIC MEASURING
### L. A. SAYCE
## AN INTRODUCTION TO AUTOMATION
### J. A. ADDERLEY
## AUTOMATION IN THE SUGAR INDUSTRY
### R. M. J. WITHERS

*Technology in Medicine*

## THE TECHNOLOGY OF HEART SURGERY
### DENIS MELROSE
## THE PHARMACEUTICAL INDUSTRY
### ALASTAIR GRAHAM

*Reporting Technology*

## LET'S MAKE UP THE WORDS AS WE GO ALONG
### D. M. DESOUTTER

# GUIDE TO THE BRITISH ECONOMY
## PETER DONALDSON

*Guide to the British Economy* is intended for the general reader who would like to have some grasp of what economics is about and what makes the economy tick, but who may find the textbook approach unpalatably abstract. Economic ideas, therefore, are presented here within the real context of the British economy. The aim is both to give an impression of the working of the different elements in the economy and to illustrate the extent to which economic analysis can be helpful in solving the problems which face policy-makers.

In the first part of this introductory guide Peter Donaldson is mainly concerned with matters of finance, including the stock-market. After a full examination of industry, labour, and trade, he goes on, in the final section of the book, to a general discussion of economic theories, their scope, and limitations.

# ECONOMIC PLANNING AND DEMOCRACY

## FIRMIN OULÈS

The currents of economic planning and democratic freedom run counter. Hence one of our acutest dilemmas.

Professor Oulès, leader of 'The New Lausanne School' of economists, faces this difficulty squarely in a new Pelican in which he effectively 'demystifies' the economic complex of Western Europe, laying bare the forces which determine the array of facts and figures we call economics. His examination is both honest and intelligent, and he comments forcefully on the anti-democratic trend of 'indicative planning', as practised notably in France.

As an alternative Professor Oulès makes his own recommendation. It is for 'planning by enlightenment' – a concept which combines budgetary coordination, at the national level, with the systematic provision of enough data for industry, finance, commerce, and labour to act rationally yet freely.

*Economic Planning and Democracy* is at once a brilliantly clear exposition of the material realities of trade and industry and a constructive solution of a problem which is today admitted by most politicians and economists.

# ATTITUDES IN BRITISH MANAGEMENT
## A P.E.P. REPORT

Efficient industry is in the hands of the managers. With this in mind the research staff of P.E.P. recently interviewed 300 senior executives in industries ranging from domestic appliances to shipbuilding. They wanted to find out which industrial practices 'appeared to be conducive to growth'. *Attitudes in British Management* is the report of their findings.

Managers, it appears, fall naturally into two categories: 'thrusters' and 'sleepers' . . . those who meet problems as challenges and those who allow their firms to stagnate. Many of the reasons for success or failure are suggested by the verbatim answers given to P.E.P.'s questions by men actively involved in the conduct of industry.

If Britain is to revitalize her economy, most of the answers are here. Can they be applied?

(This P.E.P. report was written by Anthony Gater, David Insull, Harold Lind, and Peter Seglow, of the research staff.)

# INDUSTRY IN THE U.S.A.

## GEOFFREY OWEN

What is it that places American industry, as a whole, so far ahead of the world? The talent of businessmen, the good sense of unions, the attitude of government, the intensity of competition, or just a wealth of raw materials? This new Pelican takes a dispassionate look at how American industry is managed, how the key decisions are reached, and how managers are trained (at institutions like the Harvard Business School) to make these decisions; what lessons, the author asks, can Britain learn from American experience?

The book emphasizes the high esteem in which business has always been held in the United States – hence the high calibre of American businessmen. At the same time, the author argues, actions by government have made a big contribution to American prosperity.

Geoffrey Owen represented the *Financial Times* in America for three years before his appointment as Industrial Editor. In this study of the roots of the American success story, he compares the men and methods he saw at work there with their European counterparts.